W9-CKI-545

## CLASSIC WARPLANES

# GENERAL DYNAMICS
# F-16
# FIGHTING
# FALCON

## Doug Richardson

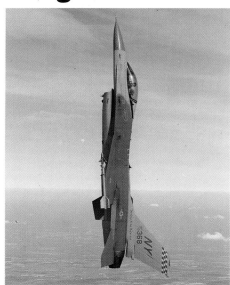

# GALLERY BOOKS

An Imprint of W. H. Smith Publishers Inc.
112 Madison Avenue
New York City 10016

## A SALAMANDER BOOK

© Salamander Books Ltd. 1990
129/137 York Way,
London N7 9LG,
United Kingdom.

ISBN 0–8317–14018

This edition published in 1990 by Gallery
Books, an imprint of W. H. Smith Publishers,
Inc., 112 Madison Avenue, New York, New
York 10016.

Gallery Books are available for bulk purchase
for sales promotions and premium use.
For details, write or telephone the Manager of
Special Sales, W. H. Smith Publishers, Inc.,
112 Madison Avenue, New York, New York
10016. (212) 532-6600

All rights reserved. Except for use in a review,
no part of this book may be reproduced, stored
in a retrieval system or transmitted in any form
or by any means, electronic, mechanical,
photocopying or otherwise, without the prior
permission of the publisher.

All correspondence concerning the content
of this volume should be addressed to
Salamander Books Ltd.

This book may not be sold outside the
United States of America or Canada.

## CREDITS

Editor: Bob Munro
Designers: Oxprint Ltd, England
Color artwork: TIGA, Michael Keep
(© Salamander Books Ltd)
Three-view and cutaway drawings: © Pilot
Press Ltd, England
Scrap line drawings: Mike Badrocke
(© Salamander Books Ltd)
Filmset: Oxprint Ltd, England; The Old Mill,
England; Flairplan Typesetting Ltd, England
Color separation: Graham Curtis Repro,
England
Printed in Belgium by Proost International
Book Production

## AUTHOR

DOUG RICHARDSON is a defense journalist and author specializing in the fields of aviation, guided missiles and electronics. After a successful career as an electronics and aerospace engineer he moved into journalism. He has been the Defense Editor of "Flight International", Editor of "Military Technology", and Editor of "Defense Materiel" before becoming a full-time freelance writer.

He 'has written many Salamander books including "The Illustrated Guide to Electronic Warfare", "The F-16 Fact-File", "The AH-1 Fact File", "An Illustrated Survey of the West's Modern Fighters" and "Stealth Warplanes".

# CONTENTS

On paper, it was a classic mis-match: the unparalleled military prowess of the United States against an ill-equipped guerilla force. In reality, the Vietnam war was a nightmare for the US military forces. All too often their massive superiority in both manpower and fire-power was found wanting; ill-suited to taking on and beating the Viet Cong. Nowhere was this harsh reality better illustrated than in the realm of air-to-air combat in the skies above North Vietnam.

While the North Vietnamese were flying lightweight and agile Soviet designs such as the Mikoyan-Gurevich MiG-17 Fresco and MiG-21 Fishbed, the US was countering with aircraft such as the Republic F-105 Thunderchief and McDonnell Douglas F-4 Phantom II. Such aircraft were the result of a long-held belief that "bigger is better", but in practice, no amount of air-to-air missiles (AAMs) and cannons could compensate

**Below: Small, light and extremely manoeuvrable, the North American F-86 Sabre spearheaded the West's first generation of jet fighters.**

for the fact that they were heavy and less manoeuvrable than their Soviet-built adversaries.

Yet it had not always been this way. The Korean War had seen the concept of the lightweight fighter put into practice. In order to cope with the threat posed by the small but potent MiG-15 Fagot, the US Air Force (USAF) had sent its latest fighter, the North American F-86A Sabre, into combat. The subsequent air superiority enjoyed was further guaranteed in the summer of 1951 with the combat debut of the F-86E. The threat posed by the subsonic MiG-15s had been dealt with effectively, but the US realized that it was only a matter of time before transonic or even supersonic Soviet fighters emerged.

North American was already looking to the future as the first of the F-86As were making their combat debut over Korea, and in January 1951 the company made an unsolicited proposal to the USAF for a supersonic "Sabre 45". In a matter of months, the idea had been given the go-ahead and was designated the F-100.

Rather appropriately it was named the Super Sabre, but at twice the weight of an

F-86 loaded for take-off some USAF officials worried that it would be too complex and expensive for use as a basic day fighter. They were right: the F-100, successful as it was, would serve primarily as a fighter-bomber.

Seemingly more suited to the air combat role was the Lockheed F-104 Starfighter: a response to a 1952 USAF requirement for a lightweight supersonic day fighter. It was relatively small, highly manoeuvrable and very fast (the first Mach 2+ aircraft to enter USAF service), but a high crash rate and limited operational flexibility at a time when the concept of the multi-role fighter was in vogue led to Air Force disillusionment and cuts in procurement. Though the F-104C did see brief service over Vietnam in the mid-60s, it soon gave way to another, quite different type of fighter.

The McDonnell Douglas F-4 Phantom II had started life as a US Navy fighter, but the Air Force was soon placing large orders to meet its fighter needs and it was to operate in a diversity of combat roles in the air war over Vietnam. When it came to air-to-air combat, however, the F-4 was

**Left: The USAF's need for a fighter with supersonic capabilities led to the development and procurement of Lockheed's F-104 Starfighter.**

Western eyes, including a high-performance, twin-finned interceptor far superior to any other Soviet fighter – the Mach 3-capable MiG-25 Foxbat. For the USAF, the goal now was to produce a dedicated air superiority fighter able to out-fly and out-fight the hottest fighters which the Soviet Union could field in the 1970s and early 1980s.

## EAGLE DEVELOPMENT

The result was a contract awarded to McDonnell Douglas covering the development of what became the F-15 Eagle: a 40,000lb (18,141kg) single-seat, twin-engined, fixed-wing fighter to replace the F-4E in front-line air defence. The ADF concept had taken a back seat, but the idea still had support from a group who doubted the wisdom of relying on a large, complex and expensive design.

Led by Major John Boyd, a former fighter pilot and air combat tactics instructor, and Pierre Sprey, a civilian weapon systems analyst in the Office of the Assistant Secretary of Defense, Systems Analysis (OASD/SA), this group

found wanting, and the reasons lay not only in the fact that this was another product of the "big size, big budget" school of fighter design.

The F-4 embodied much of this unrealistic philosophy. Weighing in at over 50,000lb (22,675kg), this brute of a machine could not match the agility of the much lighter MiGs. To make matters worse, no provision was made for an integral cannon; instead, the Air Force put its faith in missiles such as the AIM-7 Sparrow and AIM-9 Sidewinder. However, the reality of air-to-air engagements over Vietnam provided a rude awakening for the Air Force, and the F-4 was soon making good use of a multi-barrel cannon and wing leading-edge manoeuvring slats.

Nevertheless, the Air Force had learnt the hard way that a new air superiority fighter was urgently needed, and so set about the concept formulation studies of what were known as the FX (Fighter Experimental) and the ADF (Advanced Day Fighter). The former was initially

**Right: Unveiled in 1967, the twin-engined MiG-25 Foxbat startled the West with performance figures far in excess of other Soviet fighters.**

visualized as a 60,000lb (27,211kg) twin-engined design with a variable-geometry wing; the ADF was to be a lightweight design of around 25,000lb (11,338kg), with a wing loading and thrust-to-weight ratio which would better the performance of the MiG-21 by around 25 per cent.

Though the two projects were being developed in unison, events in the Soviet Union in 1967 were to influence the pace of development in favour of the FX. In July of that year, the Soviets revealed several new front-line military aircraft to

# History and Development

– known as the "Lightweight Fighter Mafia" within the Pentagon – believed that the future of fighter design lay in a return to smaller, simpler, highly-manoeuvrable machines. Such designs would be cheaper to build and operate, thus allowing larger numbers to be deployed in service – an important consideration when trying to counter the numerical superiority of Warsaw Pact air forces.

Applying their ideas to the existing FX project, Boyd and Sprey believed that a smaller fighter weighing 33,000 to 35,000lb (14,966 to 15,873kg) could be produced with superior all-round performance. They presented their ideas to the Air Force in spring 1968, but without success; supporters of the FX project saw the "Fighter Mafia's" views as a threat to their cherished new fighter and rejected their proposals. Undeterred, Boyd and Sprey conceived a completely new, single-engined design weighing in at approximately 25,000lb (11,338kg) which Sprey dubbed the F-XX.

Though the Air Force remained sceptical, widespread criticism of high-risk, high-cost Department of Defense (DoD) weapon systems development and procurement policies had led to an official investigation, followed by the publication of an official report in July 1970 which included many recommendations on how to improve the procurement process. One such recommendation called for a return to competitive prototyping, whereby new designs could be flight-tested against each other before any full-scale development was approved, rather than awarding contracts for prototypes of a single design. Such a system had given way in the 1960s to an unhealthy reliance on masses of paper studies and theoretical analyses, and the awarding of contracts for the construction of prototypes of a single design. All too often this approach proved to be far too costly and time-consuming.

**Below: An F-4E Phantom II flanked by a pair of F-15 Eagle interceptors: two fighter designs which, despite their undoubted capabilities, embody many features of the "bigger is better" school of fighter design.**

The Air Force, noting this political enthusiasm, was also beginning to take action, and in May 1971 the Air Force Prototype Study Group was formally established. Ironically, Major John Boyd, one of the founders of the "Fighter Mafia", was a key member of the group, and he was able to push the concept of a new lightweight fighter. This, along with five other programmes, was highlighted by the group for possible funding in their final report to the DoD.

## LWF FUNDING

In the event, $12 million was provided in the 1972 Defense Budget to cover work on only two of the six programmes. One was for a transport aircraft to replace the Lockheed C-130 Hercules; the other was for a lightweight fighter (LWF).

The official Request for Proposals (RFP) for the fighter project (now officially known as the Lightweight Fighter Prototype Programme) was issued to the aerospace industry on 6 January 1972, and companies used to responding to detailed specifications of tightly-defined aircraft found themselves being asked to work to a very different set of rules.

The new aircraft were to be technology demonstrators rather than fighter prototypes, and were to include a mixture of new and off-the-shelf technologies in order to minimize development risks while providing experience of new technologies which the DoD could incorporate in future fighter designs, lightweight or otherwise. Design teams were free to take chances which they might not have risked had an immediate production contract for a winning design been at stake.

This was an important decision, for the F-15 Eagle's high manoeuvrability and performance had been achieved by use of relatively conventional design concepts: a large wing to provide lots of lift, plus two high thrust-to-weight ratio turbofan engines which would give lots of propulsive power for a minimum fuel burn. By the time the LWF programme came

**Above: Smaller and far more agile than most Western machines, the MiG-21 Fishbed cruelly exposed the limitations of the larger US fighters during the Vietnam War.**

around, aircraft designers were ready to evaluate newer technologies which promised to boost performance, but which had been thought too risky or immature for use in the F-15 Eagle.

Studies of the air battles of the Vietnam, Six Day and Indo-Pakistan Wars had shown that fighters rarely used high supersonic speeds or extreme altitudes. The Air Force concluded that most future air combat would take place at speeds of Mach 0.6 to 1.6 and altitudes of 30,000 to 40,000ft (9,150 to 12,200m); so the new fighter was to be optimized for these conditions rather than for top speeds in the region of Mach 2 and a combat ceiling of 50,000ft (15,250m) or more, both of which were available from the F-15.

Additionally, emphasis was to be placed on good turn rate (especially in the region of Mach 0.9 to 1.2), acceleration

and range. Given this capability, the Air Force believed that the LWF would be able to successfully counter existing Warsaw Pact aircraft such as the MiG-21 Fishbed, MiG-23 Flogger and Sukhoi Su-7 Fitter, as well as future designs.

Getting the size and weight of the aircraft right was an important consideration for all of the competitors: keeping both down helps achieve the best thrust-to-weight ratio for any given powerplant, and the RFP called for an overall gross weight of approximately 20,000lb (9,070 kg). Size would also have an important influence on unit costs: the smaller a fighter is, the cheaper it is likely to be to produce, and the RFP called for an average flyaway unit cost of $3 million for any production version.

The $3 million price-tag was based on a purchase of 300 units of any production LWF spread over 3 years, but there was no obligation on the part of the Air Force to place any orders. Nevertheless, five companies – Boeing, General Dynamics, Lockheed, Northrop and Vought – responded to the RFP by the 18 February

deadline; all aware of the potential for orders both at home and abroad, particularly from several European nations which would soon have to find a replacement for the many F-104 Starfighters then in service.

Following analysis of the various proposals, the Air Force announced that the General Dynamics (GD) Model 401 and the Northrop P-600 had emerged as the winners. Both GD and Northrop received funding ($37,943,000 and $39,878,715 respectively) to cover the development and flight-testing of two prototypes each. At the same time, military deignations were applied: the Model 401 became the YF-16, and the P-600 was to be known as the YF-17. Use of the "Y" (development) prefix instead of the "XF-" designation traditionally applied to fighter prototypes was deliberate, reflecting the fact that the new aircraft were to use both off-the-shelf and experimental technologies.

## TAKING SHAPE

On paper, both designs were to be technology demonstrators, but GD could see that a production version was likely to follow. At the company's headquarters in Fort Worth, Texas, it was agreed that a careful blend of old and new technology would be needed to achieve the performance the Air Force was looking for, as well as the confidence that a developed version could be produced at the right cost and be combat effective.

Led by Chief Project Engineer Harry Hillaker, the GD design team set themselves the task of producing an aircraft to complement the F-15 force. Weighing less than 20,000lb (9,070kg), the YF-16 would provide the maximum manoeuvrability and agility possible in a small aircraft capable of conducting air combat operations at least 500nm (926km) from base.

In an attempt to meet this design objective without breaching strict cost constraints, the design team studied numerous areas where a trade-off between cost, performance or operational

# History and Development

capability would be acceptable. Keeping the size and weight down was important: the smaller a fighter is, the cheaper it is likely to be to produce. It also makes visual detection by an adversary all the more difficult and gives the best thrust-to-weight ratio for any given powerplant.

State-of-the-art technology was to be used where it was needed to provide enhanced performance, but proven components and systems were utilized wherever possible in order to avoid potential problems during the manufacturing phase. Above all, the combination of new and proven technologies was aimed at producing an aircraft which, if it won the fly-off, could then be developed into an operational fighter.

Early in the design process, GD decided to provide a stronger airframe than the Air Force had requested, creating a structure with a service life of 8,000 hours rather than the 4,000 hours specified, and able to meet a load factor of 9.0g with full internal fuel rather than the proposed 7.33g with 80 per cent internal fuel. That the company felt able to make these provisions reflected their confidence in the YF-16, and much of that was due to comprehensive theoretical analyses and wind tunnel tests covering no less than 78 variables which would have a crucial bearing on the eventual configuration of the aircraft. Among these were several parameters which would have a significant influence on the aircraft's performance capabilities.

## WING CHOICE

Choosing the right wing was difficult as it was required to meet the conflicting demands of take-offs, subsonic cruise, combat manoeuvring at high g levels, supersonic flight, and landings. The original FX studies had assumed a variable-geometry wing would be used, but GD decided to use variable-camber for the YF-16. Leading- and trailing-edge flaps would be linked to the flight control system (FCS), which was tasked with automatically adjusting flap position throughout the flight envelope, thus matching the wing to changes in speed and angle of attack (AoA). Several wing sweep angles were tested for the wing leading-edge before a figure of 40deg was eventually chosen.

Because the aircraft was to be small, space in the fuselage would be at a premium; but GD managed to maximize the internal volume available by increasing the depth of the wing towards the wing root, resulting in a smooth blend with the fuselage itself. The extra space created by this blending was used to store a substantial load of fuel and mission equipment close to the aircraft's centre of gravity (c.g.) Just how effective this proved to be can be judged by the fact that no less than 31 per cent of the weight of a loaded F-16 is made up of fuel, compared to 28 per cent for the bigger F-4 Phantom II.

Use of the wing/fuselage blending technique was not new, but a very obvious – and new – structural feature was utilized ahead of the wing. The GD design team had realized the importance of leading edge root extensions (LERX), or strakes, in enhancing the manoeuvrability of the YF-16 by producing significant trailing vortexes. At high AoA, these vortexes maintain the energy of the boundary layer air flowing over the inner section of the wing. By keeping this layer energized, the vortexes delay wing root stalling and maintain directional stability, as well as providing some forebody lift. This allowed GD to slightly reduce the size and weight of the wing, while in flight it also reduces the need for the application of drag-inducing tail trim.

**Below: Much smaller, lighter and simpler than fighters such as the F-4 and F-15, the highly distinctive General Dynamics YF-16 represented a radical about turn in US fighter design and development.**

Air intake, or inlet, behaviour would be critical at the high AoA typical in air-to-air dogfighting, and GD now knew much more about how to optimize the inlet for such conditions as well as ways of using the fuselage to help direct the airflow into the intake. A traditional multi-shock intake would give Mach 2.2 performance,

**Below: Set well back underneath the fuselage, the large air intake was a characteristic design feature of the General Dynamics fighter.**

but the Air Force was not demanding such a capability. Adopting a simpler fixed intake pattern would cut costs and save around 700lb (317kg) in weight. The eventual choice was similar to the chin intake used by Vought on their F-8 Crusader and A-7 Corsair II, but positioned well back in a ventral location aft of the cockpit.

To make the YF-16 as manoeuvrable as possible, GD decided to break one of the oldest rules in aircraft design. Since the Wright Brothers at the turn of the century, aircraft designers have always tried to make their creations inherently stable. This was achieved by making sure that the centre of pressure – the point about which wing lift is distributed – was slightly aft of the aircraft's c.g. Move the centre of pressure forward of the c.g. and the aircraft nose will tend to pitch upward, making the aircraft inherently unstable and difficult to fly. Needless to say, an aircraft which attempts to defy these simple rules of balance is likely to have a very short flying career!

At GD, breaking the traditional rules of balance was exactly what the YF-16 design team had in mind. They reasoned

**Above: The smaller size of the YF-16 is obvious as it formates on a pair of Convair F-160A Delta Darts.**

that moving the c.g. aft would reduce longitudinal stability but increase manoeuvrability. There were other benefits to be gained as well.

At supersonic speeds, an aircraft's centre of pressure moves aft; that's why, to maintain the trim, fuel is pumped aft on the Concorde airliner as it goes supersonic. On a conventional (i.e. stable) fighter, the tailplane pushes the tail down in order to maintain level flight; but at supersonic speeds, this downward force must be increased to compensate for the change in trim. This downward force detracts from overall lift, the resulting penalty being known as trim drag.

## FCS wing settings

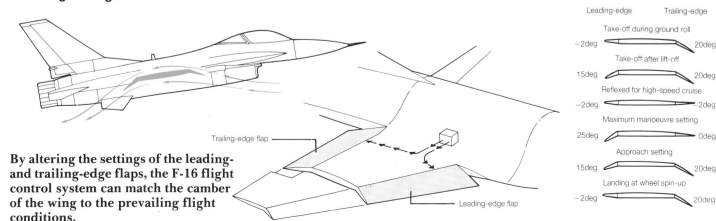

**By altering the settings of the leading- and trailing-edge flaps, the F-16 flight control system can match the camber of the wing to the prevailing flight conditions.**

Trailing-edge flap

Leading-edge flap

| Leading-edge | Trailing-edge |
| --- | --- |
| Take-off during ground roll | |
| −2deg | 20deg |
| Take-off after lift-off | |
| 15deg | 20deg |
| Reflexed for high-speed cruise | |
| −2deg | −2deg |
| Maximum manoeuvre setting | |
| 25deg | 0deg |
| Approach setting | |
| 15deg | 20deg |
| Landing at wheel spin-up | |
| −2deg | 20deg |

# History and Development

**Above: Prior to its transfer to Edwards AFB for flight-testing, the first YF-16 enters the "mouth" of the C-5A Galaxy transporter.**

The YF-16 design team believed that since the horizontal tail surfaces on an unstable aircraft need to produce less force than those on a stable aircraft, they could be made smaller and lighter. The tailplane would push up at subsonic speed, so adding to the total lift; and the tail-down force, though still required at supersonic speed, would be much less than on a stable fighter design.

With conventional mechanical controls, the inherently unstable YF-16 would be all but impossible to fly, as the surfaces linked to such controls move in response to the pilot's inputs. On the YF-16, GD engineers installed a fly-by-wire (FBW), stability augmentation and flight-control system (FCS), with the pilot's control inputs being passed to a computer which would calculate how the various control surfaces were to be moved in order to achieve the desired response.

Elimination of the mechanical controls was to make severe demands on computer reliability, and if the "relaxed stability" system was to be accepted by potential operators, the FBW system had to be at least as reliable as the mechanical linkages it was replacing. As mechanical controls are, by their very nature, highly reliable, the use of multiple channels was seen as one way of boosting the reliability of the new system.

## FBW CHOICE

Since the YF-16 would have no mechanical flight controls, GD decided to install a quadruplex (four-channel) FBW system, along with analogue electronics. Failure of one channel would leave the remaining three operating normally – the equivalent of a triplex system. The rival Northrop YF-17 also used a quadruplex analogue FBW system, but being a naturally stable design it was able to retain mechanical back-up controls.

The cockpit of the YF-16 was also to break new ground in fighter design. Like the F-15 Eagle, it would have a single-piece canopy, giving the pilot superb all-round visibility; but within the cockpit, two features were to set the GD aircraft apart from the Eagle and all previous US production fighters.

The first feature was the semi-reclining position chosen for the pilot's ejection seat. Research suggested that use of a reclining seat could increase the pilot's tolerance to high-g manoeuvres by reducing the separation in height between the pilot's head and heels, so GD installed an ejection seat with a tilt of 30deg. The idea worked and

was subsequently retained, but it is significant that later US fighters were to make use of a conventional ejection seat as it was found that the high position of the pilot's knees when seated in the tilted seat reduced the effective area available for controls and displays.

The second novel feature in the YF-16 cockpit was the adoption of a sidestick controller located on the starboard side of the cockpit, in place of the traditional centrally-mounted control column. Seen as an essential aid to the pilot when flying under high-g conditions, the sidestick was originally designed to be force-sensitive and did not move at all.

Fielding all of these features on the YF-16 may have been a gamble, but as the project's Director of Engineering William C. Deitz was to observe later: "If we hadn't put them in the prototype, we'd still be arguing about putting them into a production airplane."

The first of the two YF-16 prototypes was rolled out at General Dynamics' Forth Worth manufacturing plant on 13 December 1973, just 21 months after funding had been allocated. Following transfer to the Air Force Flight Test

**Above: Highlighting the contrasts between two generations of fighter design, the YF-16 is almost dwarfed by an accompanying RF-4 during a test flight from Edwards AFB.**

Center (AFFTC) at Edwards AFB, California, the "official" first flight took place on 2 February 1974 with GD test pilot Phil Oestricher at the controls. Actually, the aircraft had flown for the first time on 20 January during what should have been high-speed taxi trials conducted firmly on the ground! As the speed built up, the nose was raised as planned; but a roll control oscillation built up during the run, causing the tail of the port wingtip missile and the starboard horizontal stabilator to scrape the runway.

Given the aircraft's increasing speed and the fact that it was now heading off of the runway into the sand, Oestricher decided it would be prudent to get airborne. After a brief six-minute sortie over the California desert, he landed successfully, much to the relief of the support personnel on the ground, and, no doubt, himself.

On the official first flight, Oestricher took the YF-16 up to 15,000ft (4,575m) with the undercarriage extended. The gear was then retracted, the speed increased, and a series of 2-3g turns executed. During the third flight three days later the aircraft went supersonic for the first time, as well as pulling a series of 5g manoeuvres.

The second YF-16 prototype took to the air for the first time on 9 May 1974, followed exactly a month later by the maiden flight of the the first of Northrop's YF-17 prototypes (the second YF-17 flew on 21 August). By now the LWF had been renamed the Agile Combat Fighter (ACF), with the original technology demonstration programme being superceded by a straightforward competition between the two designs. The stakes were high, with substantial orders for the winner very likely to follow.

The Air Force had not intended to select the winning design until May 1975, but the European factor changed that. Around the time that the second YF-16 took to the air, a delegation from four North Atlantic Treaty Organization (NATO) countries – Belgium, Denmark,

**Above: Though it lost out to the YF-16 in the USAF's ACF fly-off, Northrop's YF-17 would eventually be developed into the F/A-18 for the US Navy and Marine Corps.**

the Netherlands and Norway – visited the United States to discuss future procurement plans. It was agreed that if the USAF placed orders for a production version of the eventual ACF competition winner, the four NATO nations (known collectively as the European Participation Group: EPG) would, assuming evaluation of other designs proved unsuccessful, place orders for the same aircraft.

Such a deal was attractive to both sides: the NATO nations had built the F-104G Starfighter under licence, and were now looking for a replacement for the Lockheed design on the production lines and in front-line squadrons; and the United States was keen to see its allies boost their air strength with a large-scale purchase which would help drive down the cost of the winning ACF design. The Europeans could not wait until the Air Force's May 1975 deadline, so a compromise date of early 1975 was agreed and testing of both designs was accelerated.

Just two weeks into 1975, Secretary of the Air Force John McLucas announced that the General Dynamics YF-16 had won the ACF competition, the flight-test programme having revealed the performance of the YF-16 to be "significantly better" than that of the YF-17, particularly at near-supersonic and super-

sonic speeds. It also proved to have better acceleration and endurance; was up to 15 seconds faster in a climb to 30,000ft (9,150m); and offered the best rate of turn, except at around Mach 0.7 where the YF-17 proved able to out-turn its rival. The Air Force also believed the YF-16 to be closer to a final production configuration than the YF-17, particularly in areas such as weight, fuel capacity and thrust-to-weight ratio.

## INITIAL ORDERS

Shortly after the winning design had been announced, the USAF confirmed its intention to procure no less than 650 production examples, thus guaranteeing additional orders on behalf of the four NATO air arms. These came on 7 June 1975, with orders for 348 aircraft (116 for Belgium; 58 for Denmark; 102 for the Netherlands; and 72 for Norway) being formally announced at the Paris Air Show.

The production aircraft was in effect a slightly enlarged version of the prototype.

# History and Development

The YF-16 had not been fitted with a nose-mounted radar, but the F-16 would field the Westinghouse APG-66, a medium-pulse repetition frequency (PRF) pulse-Doppler set which had won a competitive fly-off with a Hughes radar.

The APG-66 was larger than the set originally planned for use in the F-16, so to make room the nose of the F-16 would be lengthened by 7in (17.8cm) and the diameter increased by 4in (10.1cm). The overall length of the fuselage was extended by 10in (25.4cm), while the wing area was increased by 20sq ft (1.86m²) and fitted with an additional pair of hardpoints. The stabilators were also increased in size, extra access doors were added to the airframe, and the F100 powerplant was fitted with a jet starter.

Needless to say, these changes all added to the weight of the aircraft: the initial production F-16 was to weigh in at around 24,460lb (11,092kg), an increase of more than 20 per cent on the original target maximum of 20,000lb (9,080kg).

Following the EPG's decision to order the F-16, a Memorandum of Understanding (MoU) between the US and EPG governments was drawn up covering the establishment of two European F-16 production lines.

One was to be at the Fokker plant at Schipol-Oost, in the Netherlands; the other at the Société Anonyme Belge de Constructions Aéronautiques (SABCA) facility in Gossellies, Belgium. It was agreed that these lines would produce 184 and 164 aircraft respectively, thus completing the (initial) EPG order, as well as taking an agreed share of the work on aircraft ordered by the USAF and any future export customers.

**Above: Following victory, a batch of full-scale development F-16s was produced, the first (nearest) and second of which are seen during a perfect formation take-off.**

**Below: Activity on the shop floor at Fokker's Schipol-Oost plant in the Netherlands. Co-ordination and management of the multi-national programme was a formidable task.**

## F-16 European co-production

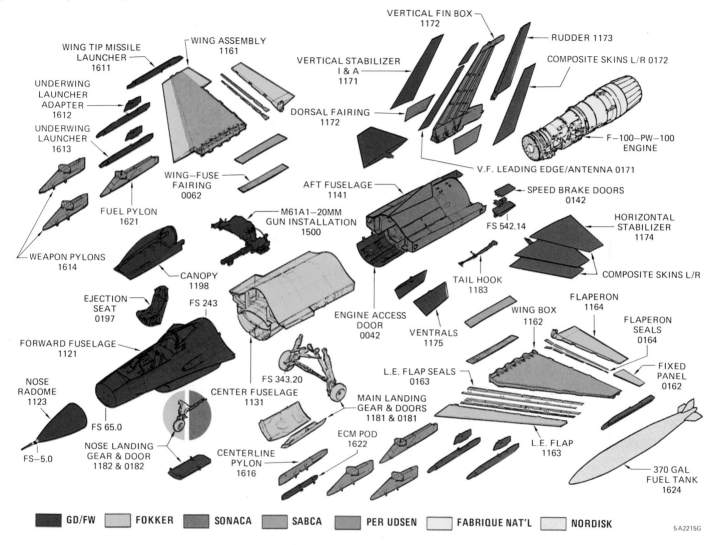

WING TIP MISSILE LAUNCHER 1611
WING ASSEMBLY 1161
VERTICAL FIN BOX 1172
RUDDER 1173
VERTICAL STABILIZER I & A 1171
COMPOSITE SKINS L/R 0172
UNDERWING LAUNCHER ADAPTER 1612
UNDERWING LAUNCHER 1613
DORSAL FAIRING 1172
F-100-PW-100 ENGINE
WING-FUSE FAIRING 0062
AFT FUSELAGE 1141
V.F. LEADING EDGE/ANTENNA 0171
FUEL PYLON 1621
M61A1-20MM GUN INSTALLATION 1500
SPEED BRAKE DOORS 0142
FS 542.14
HORIZONTAL STABILIZER 1174
WEAPON PYLONS 1614
CANOPY 1198
TAIL HOOK 1183
COMPOSITE SKINS L/R
EJECTION SEAT 0197
FS 243
ENGINE ACCESS DOOR 0042
WING BOX 1162
FLAPERON 1164
FLAPERON SEALS 0164
FORWARD FUSELAGE 1121
VENTRALS 1175
FIXED PANEL 0162
NOSE RADOME 1123
L.E. FLAP SEALS 0163
FS 65.0
CENTER FUSELAGE 1131
MAIN LANDING GEAR & DOORS 1181 & 0181
L.E. FLAP 1163
FS-5.0
NOSE LANDING GEAR & DOOR 1182 & 0182
CENTERLINE PYLON 1616
ECM POD 1622
FS 343.20
370 GAL FUEL TANK 1624

GD/FW    FOKKER    SONACA    SABCA    PER UDSEN    FABRIQUE NAT'L    NORDISK

5A2215G

**Above: An early breakdown of the F-16 manufacturing and assembly effort, clearly illustrating the responsibilities of no less than seven principal participants.**

Following start-up of the Belgian line in February 1978 (the Dutch line was to achieve this milestone in April 1978) an F-16 was sent over from Fort Worth for assembly tests, and by July of the same year the first Belgian components – a set of wings – had been delivered to the Texas plant. Barely a month later the first flight of a production F-16 took place at Fort Worth, followed in December by the airborne debut of the first of the Euro-built aircraft at Gosselies.

January 1979 saw the commencement of deliveries of production F-16s from all three assembly lines to service units: GD-built aircraft went to the USAF (which had increased its order to 1,388 aircraft), while SABCA started deliveries to the Belgian Air Force. The first Fokker-built F-16 took to the skies in May 1979, allowing deliveries to the Royal Netherlands Air Force to begin the following month.

The following year saw the first deliveries to Denmark and Norway from the SABCA and Fokker lines respectively, as well as to the first non-NATO customer – Israel. The new decade also saw the belated adoption of a name for the F-16. From now on it was to be known as the General Dynamics F-16 Fighting Falcon.

Most military aircraft, but especially fighters, are progressively updated and upgraded in the course of their service lives in order to meet the latest threats. In the past, this often required extensive structural redesign as the shape of the aircraft changed to accommodate more powerful engines and improved equipment. Indeed, the more successful the fighter, the more drastic the degree of airframe surgery seemed to be.

Given the complex manufacturing methods used to build the structure of a modern fighter, designers are now more reluctant to alter the shape of the aircraft. Different versions of the MiG-21 Fishbed may be easily distinguished, but its principle rival in the Vietnam war, the McDonnell Douglas F-4 Phantom II, saw much less structural alteration as the family of models grew. The systems within the F-4 were tightly packed, leaving little room for major upgrading.

General Dynamics was determined to avoid such pitfalls with the F-16. Not only did the design of the airframe include space for future systems, it also incorporated the structural features needed for planned future upgrades.

The need for an improved F-16 was spelt out to the US Congress in 1980, when Undersecretary of Defense for Research and Engineering William J. Perry described the aircraft as: "an incomplete airplane...We kidded ourselves a bit on the F-16, thinking we were buying an inexpensive fighter." The result is that although all versions of the Fighting Falcon may look nearly identical, there have in fact been nine separate production

**Right: Holding close formation over the Sierra Nevada Mountains, a quartet of early-production (Block 01) USAF F-16As make their way to the practice ranges.**

batches. Each batch is identified by a separate Block Number, and each introduced changes and improvements to enhance operational effectiveness.

Block 01 covered the first 43 production standard F-16s in Fiscal Year (FY) 1979, and was quickly followed by Block 05 (116 aicraft) and Block 10 (170 aircraft) in FY80 and FY81 respectively. These blocks were made up of F-16A/Bs, with aircraft from the different batches differing in only minor production details intended to improve overall reliability and maintainability. A subsequent modification programme in effect between 1982 and 1984 saw Block 01 and 05 aircraft brought up to Block 10 standard.

Production of Block 15 aircraft started in late 1981 and saw the introduction of some quite major changes to the aircraft as part of Multinational Staged Improvement Plan I (MSIP I). First approved during February 1981, this programme covered internal and external changes under Engineering Change Proposals (ECP) 350 and 425, and was to add approximately 200lb (90.7kg) to the overall weight of the F-16.

Few of the modifications introduced by ECP350 had an initial impact on the F-16, although the engine inlet structure was strengthened and the load capacity of the centre underwing pylons was increased by 1,000lb (453.5kg) to 3,500lb (1,587kg). The aircraft's environmental control system (ECS) was also modified to increase system efficiency, thus improving cockpit conditions for the pilot.

**Above: As part of ECP350, the F-16 wing was modified to permit the carriage and launch of the Hughes AIM-120A AMRAAM, an example of which is seen during launch.**

Most of the ECP350 changes were intended to prepare the airframe for new equipment and weaponry which would be added from the mid-1980s onwards. The structure and wiring of the wings was modified to allow the carriage of the AIM-120 Advanced Medium-Range Air-

### Stabilator configurations

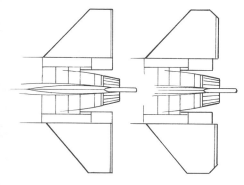

**Above: As a result of ECP425, the original stabilator pattern (left) gave way to a new configuration.**

to-Air Missile (AMRAAM), while new hard-points located on either side of the engine intake would one day carry the Low-Altitude Navigation and Targetting with Infra-Red at Night (LANTIRN) electro-optical (EO) system. Structural changes and new wiring within the cockpit cleared the way for future new displays, while other modifications prepared the fuselage to receive a planned new radar altimeter and electronic warfare (EW) suite.

Early service experience with the F-16A had shown that carriage of heavy munition loads moved the aircraft's c.g. forward. This had the effect of making the aircraft more stable and thus more difficult to manoeuvre. To overcome this problem, ECP425 was introduced.

Under this part of MSIP I, the original pattern of the stabilators was replaced with a new design of increased area. Cheaper materials and a new design process were also introduced, thus overcoming a shortage of titanium and saving money at the same time. The tailplane spar was now made from aluminium rather than titanium, and the carbon-fibre skins were now mechanically fastened to a corrugated aluminium alloy filling, rather than being bonded to a standard aluminium honeycomb filling.

**Below: Immediately noticeable in the F-16's uncluttered cockpit is the absence of a central control column, this having given way to a side-stick controller on the right.**

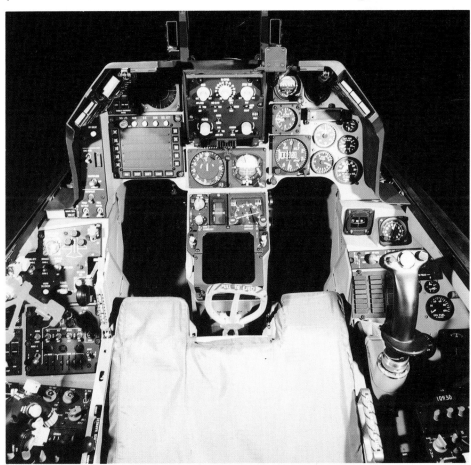

# Developing the Breed

The need for a braking parachute led GD to modify the base of the vertical fin to incorporate a fairing for this item should customers so desire.

Following completion of Block 15 production in 1987, Block 15 Operational Capability Upgrade (OCU) was introduced. Again covering F-16A/Bs, this added a radar altimeter, expanded computer memory capacity, a wide-angle head-up display (HUD) as used in the F-15C/D, and provision for the carriage and use of the highly-effective Penguin Mk 3 anti-ship missile (ASM).

Production of Block 15 OCU aircraft is scheduled to end in the second half of 1992, the final aircraft going to the Pakistan Air Force; but under a modification programme started in 1987, some Block 10 and Block 15 aircraft will be upgraded to this standard, with the work not expected to end until late-1993.

During 1989, a major rebuild programme affecting 270 existing F-16As was introduced under the title of Block 15 Advanced Day Fighter (ADF), the aircraft involved having been selected to serve with the Air National Guard (ANG) as interceptors. With this in mind, provision was made for the use of the AIM-7 Sparrow air-to-air missile (AAM) and the AIM-120 AMRAAM, as well as introducing an improved Identification Friend or Foe (IFF) system and a high-frequency (HF) radio. The Westinghouse APG-66 radar has also been improved to facilitate operations with the medium-range missiles noted, and a night-identification searchlight has been installed.

All of the Blocks previously detailed involved production of the F-16A (single-seat) and F-16B (two-seat) models; in the second half of 1984, Block 25 introduced the F-16C and F-16D under MSIP II.

**Above: The exceptionally clean lines of the F-16 are clearly evident in this view of two 134th TFS/Vermont ANG F-16As. Several ANG squadrons have replaced their F-4s and F-106s with an ADF variant of the F-16A.**

**Below: Successive production blocks have greatly enhanced the fighting capabilities of the F-16. This is a Block 40 F-16C, armed with the AGM-88A HARM for use in the "Wild Weasel" defence-suppression role.**

These models introduced the new Westinghouse APG-68 radar, a wide-angle HUD, two new multi-mode cathode ray tube (CRT) cockpit displays, and provision for the use of the AGM-65D Imaging Infra-Red (IIR) version of the Maverick air-to-ground missile (AGM).

Another improvement saw the replacement of the analogue FBW system used on all previous F-16s with an all-new quadruplex (four-channel) digital system with no mechanical back-up.

## ENGINE OPTIONS

Block 25 production lasted until mid-1986, and was followed by the first of the Block 30/32 machines in a programme which ran until mid-1989. These aircraft (again a mix of F-16C/Ds) were the first to have a revised engine bay able to accept rival engine designs, namely the 23,770lb (10,780kg) thrust General Electric F110-GE-100 (Block 30) or the more powerful

28,984lb (13,144kg) thrust Pratt & Whitney F100-PW-220 (Block 32).

To provide the extra airflow demanded by the P&W engine, the air intake was enlarged. Experience later showed that this change could create stability problems when the aircraft was flown at high AoA with a 300 US gal (1,135 litre) centreline fuel tank in place. During trials to investigate this, an aircraft was almost lost, pulling out of a dangerous spin which had lost 23,000ft (7,015m) and taken the pilot to within seconds of ejection height. Changes to the aircraft's yaw limiter finally cleared the problem, and a retrofit was drawn up for all F-16C/Ds.

Block 30/32 also introduced seal-bond fuel tanks, an expanded computer memory, plus facilities for the use of the AIM-120 AMRAAM and AGM-45 Shrike anti-radiation missile (ARM).

Current F-16 production comes under Block 40/42, with the dual title again indicating installation of the GE or P&W

**Above: With suitable inscriptions to highlight its night-fighting capabilities, the first Block 40 F-16C displays its intake-mounted LANTIRN EO nav-attack pods. Mounted on the underwing pylons are AGM-65D Maverick IR-guided missiles.**

powerplant. All Block 40/42 aircraft are equipped with the improved Westinghouse APG-68(V) radar and LANTIRN EO nav-attack pods, thus allowing them to fly terrain-following flight paths. Other changes include adding a LANTIRN-compatible wide-angle HUD based on diffractive optics, an expanded (256K) fire control computer, a global positioning system (GPS) satellite navigation (sat/nav) unit, a quadruplex digital FBW flight control system (FCS), and the ability to carry the AGM-88A high-speed anti-radiation missile (HARM).

Block 40/42 aircraft are also able to operate at higher take-off weights,

# Developing the Breed

## General Dynamics F-16C (Block 42) Fighting Falcon cutaway drawing key

1 Pitot head/air data probe
2 Glassfibre radome
3 Lightning conducting strips
4 Planar radar scanner
5 Radome hinge point, opens to starboard
6 Scanner tracking mechanism
7 ILS glideslope aerial
8 Radar mounting bulkhead
9 Incidence vane, port and starboard
10 IFF aerial
11 GBU-15 laser-guided glide bomb
12 AN/APG-68 digital pulse-doppler, multi-mode radar electronics equipment bay
13 Radar warning antennae, port and starboard
14 Front pressure bulkhead
15 Static ports
16 Fuselage forebody strake fairing
17 Forward avionics equipment bay
18 Canopy jettison charge
19 Instrument panel shroud
20 Instrument panel, multifunction CRT head-down-displays
21 Side-stick controller (fly-by-wire control system)
22 Video recorder
23 GEC wide-angle head-up-display
24 Penguin air-to-surface anti-shipping missile (Norwegian aircraft)
25 LAU-3A 19-round rocket launcher
26 2·75-in (68-mm) FFAR
27 ATLIS II laser designating and ranging pod
28 Intake flank (No 5R) stores pylon adapter
29 LANTIRN (FLIR) targetting pod
30 Frameless bubble canopy
31 Ejection seat headrest
32 McDonnell-Douglas ACES II zero-zero ejection seat
33 Side console panel
34 Canopy frame fairing
35 Canopy external emergency release
36 Engine throttle lever incorporating HOTAS (hands-on-throttle-and-stick) radar controls
37 Canopy jettison handle
38 Cockpit section frame construction
39 Boundary layer splitter plate
40 Fixed geometry air intake
41 Nosewheel, aft retracting
42 LANTIRN (FLIR/TFR) navigation pod
43 Port intake flank (No 5L) stores pylon adapter
44 Forward position light
45 Rapport III threat warning antenna fairing (Belgian and Israeli aircraft)
46 Intake duct framing
47 Gun gas suppression muzzle aperture
48 Aft avionics equipment bay
49 Cockpit rear pressure bulkhead
50 Canopy hinge point
51 Ejection seat rails
52 Canopy rotary actuator
53 Conditioned air outlet duct
54 Canopy sealing frame
55 Canopy aft glazing
56 600-US gal (500-lmp gal/2 271-l) long range fuel tank
57 Garrett turbine emergency power unit (EPU)

58 EPU hydrazine fuel tank
59 Fuel tank bay access panel
60 Forward fuselage bag-type fuel tank. Total internal capacity 6,972 lb (3 162 kg)
61 Fuselage upper longeron
62 Conditioned air ducting
63 Cannon barrels
64 Forebody frame construction
65 Air system ground connection
66 Ventral air conditioning system equipment bay
67 Centreline 300-US gal (250-lmp gal/1 136-l) fuel tank
68 Mainwheel door hydraulic actuator
69 Mainwheel door
70 Hydraulic system ground connectors
71 Gun bay ventral gas vent
72 GE M61A1 20-mm rotary cannon
73 Ammunition feed chute
74 Hydraulic gun drive motor
75 Port hydraulic reservoir
76 Centre fuselage integral fuel tank
77 Leading-edge flap drive hydraulic motor
78 Ammunition drum, 511 rounds
79 Upper position light/refuelling floodlight
80 TACAN aerial
81 Hydraulic accumulator
82 Starboard hydraulic reservoir
83 Leading-edge flap drive shaft
84 Inboard, No 6 stores station (4,500-lb/2 041-kg capacity)
85 Pylon attachment hardpoint
86 Leading-edge flap drive shaft and rotary actuators
87 No 7 stores hardpoint (3,500-lb/1 588-kg capacity)
88 Radar warning antenna
89 Missile launch rails
90 AMRAAM air-to-air missiles
91 Loading pod (carriage of essential ground equipment and personal effects for off-base deployment)
92 Starboard leading-edge manoeuvre flap, down position
93 Outboard No 8 stores station hardpoint (700-lb/318-kg capacity)
94 Wing-tip No 9 stores station (425-lb/193-kg capacity)
95 Wing-tip AMRAAM missile
96 Starboard navigation light
97 Fixed portion of trailing edge
98 Static dischargers
99 Starboard flaperon
100 Starboard wing integral fuel tank
101 Fuel system piping
102 Fuel pump
103 Starboard wing root attachment fishplates
104 Fuel tank access panels
105 Universal air refuelling receptacle (UARSSI), open
106 Engine compressor intake centrebody fairing
107 Airframe-mounted accessory equipment gearbox
108 Jet fuel starter
109 Machined wing attachment bulkheads
110 Engine fuel management equipment

111 Pressure refuelling receptacle, ventral adapter
112 Pratt & Whitney F100-PW-220 afterburning turbofan engine
113 VHF/IFF aerial
114 Starboard flaperon hydraulic actuator
115 Fuel tank tail fins
116 Sidebody fairing integral fuel tank
117 Position light
118 Cooling air ram air intake
119 Fin root fairing
120 Forward engine support link
121 Rear fuselage integral fuel tank
122 Thermally insulated tank inner skin
123 Tank access panels
124 Radar warning system power amplifier
125 Fin root attachment fittings
126 Flight control system hydraulic accumulators
127 Multi-spar fin construction
128 Starboard all-moving tailplane (tailplane panels interchangeable)
129 General Electric F110-GE-100 alternative power plant
130 Fin leading-edge honeycomb construction
131 Dynamic pressure sensor
132 Carbon-fibre fin skin panelling
133 VHF communications aerial (AM/FM)
134 Fin-tip antenna fairing
135 Anti-collision light
136 Threat warning antennae
137 Static dischargers
138 Rudder honeycomb construction
139 Rudder hydraulic actuator
140 ECM antenna fairing
141 Tail navigation light
142 Extended tailcone fairing, brake parachute housing (Norwegian aircraft) or Rapport III or Itek 69 ECM systems (Belgian or Israeli)
143 Variable area afterburner nozzle flaps
144 Nozzle sealing fairing
145 Afterburner nozzle actuators (five)

146 Port split trailing-edge airbrake, open, upper and lower surfaces
147 Airbrake actuating linkage
148 Port all-moving tailplane
149 Static dischargers
150 Graphite-epoxy tailplane skin panels
151 Leading-edge honeycomb construction
152 Corrugated aluminium sub-structure
153 Hinge pivot fixing
154 Tailplane hydraulic actuator
155 Fuel jettison chamber, port and starboard
156 Afterburner ducting
157 Rear fuselage machined bulkheads
158 Port position light
159 AN/ALE-40 (VÖ-4) chaff/flare dispenser, port and starboard
160 Main engine thrust mounting, port and starboard
161 Sidebody fairing frame construction
162 Runway arrester hook
163 Composite construction ventral fin, port and starboard
164 Port flaperon hydraulic actuator
165 Flaperon hinges
166 Port flaperon, lowered
167 External fuel tank tail fairing
168 Flaperon honeycomb construction
169 Fixed portion of trailing edge
170 Static dischargers
171 Port navigation light
172 Wing-tip No 1 stores station (425-lb/193-kg capacity)

173 AIM-9L Sidewinder air-to-air missiles
174 AIM-7 Sparrow air-to-air missile
175 Mk 84 low drag 2,000-lb (907-kg) HE bomb
176 Mk 83 Snakeye retarded bomb
177 Missile launch rails
178 No 2 stores station (700-lb/318-kg capacity)
179 No 3 stores station (3,500-lb/1 588-kg capacity)
180 Port radar warning antenna
181 Mk 82 500-lb (227-kg) HE bombs
182 Triple ejector rack

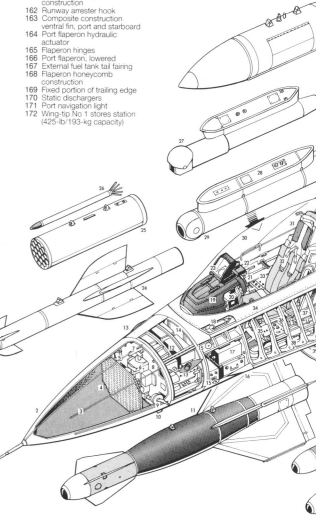

183 Wing stores pylon
184 Leading-edge manoeuvre flap honeycomb construction
185 Flap-drive shaft and rotary actuators
186 Multi-spar wing panel construction
187 Port wing integral tankage
188 No 4 stores station hardpoint (4,500-lb/2 041-kg capacity)
189 Wing root attachment fishplates

190 Undercarriage leg mounted landing lamp
191 Retraction/breaker strut
192 Main undercarriage leg strut
193 Shock absorber strut
194 Port leading-edge manoeuvre flap, down position
195 Inboard wing pylon
196 Port mainwheel, forward retracting
197 Fuel filler caps

198 370-US gal (308-Imp gal/ 1 400-l) underwing fuel tank
199 Centreline No 5 stores pylon (2,200-lb/998-kg capacity)
200 AN/ALQ-131 ECM pod
201 AGM-65 Maverick air-to-surface missile
202 Triple missile carrier/launcher

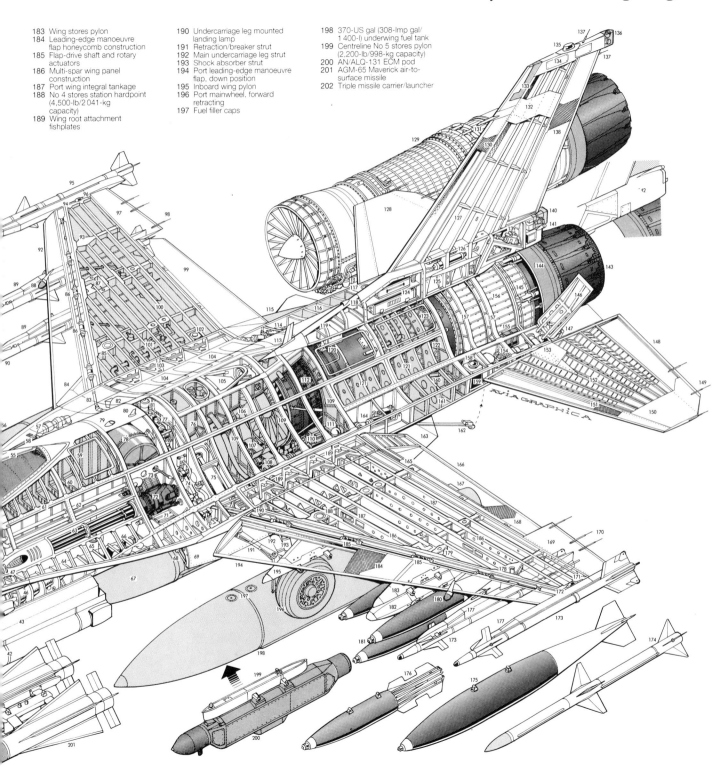

AVIAGRAPHICA

21

# Developing the Breed

**Right: Subject of intense political debate, the CAS/BAI derivative of the F-16 (known as the A-16) has the potential to significantly boost the USAF's ground-attack force. Testing of support equipment is underway.**

although this will be offset from late 1991 with the delivery of the first Block 50/52 F-16C/Ds. Aircraft from this latter block will be fitted with uprated versions of the rival GE and P&W powerplants. Designated the F110-GE-129 and F100-PW-229 respectively, both will have a maximum thrust of around 29,000lb (13,152 kg). Aircraft from this block will also be fitted with an automatic target hand-off system and the improved ALR-69 radar

**Below: In creating the M61 series of aircraft cannon, General Electric revived the rotary principle first devised by Dr. Gatling. The F-16's M61A1 is a six-barrel cannon, with a fire rate of 6,000 rds/min.**

warning receiver (RWR), and be able to carry the new HARM III missile.

In the 1990s, the USAF hopes to field a Close Air Support/Battlefield Air Interdiction (CAS/BAI) replacement for the Fairchild A-10A Thunderbolt II now in service. Several designs are being considered, but the USAF is known to favour a proposed ground attack version of the F-16, designated the A-16.

Testing of relevant equipment, particularly equipment to enhance night attack operations, is already underway. GD has carried out its own studies into possible EO sensors such as night-vision goggles, navigation/attack FLIR systems, and the transmission of data to the pilot via helmet-mounted sights and displays.

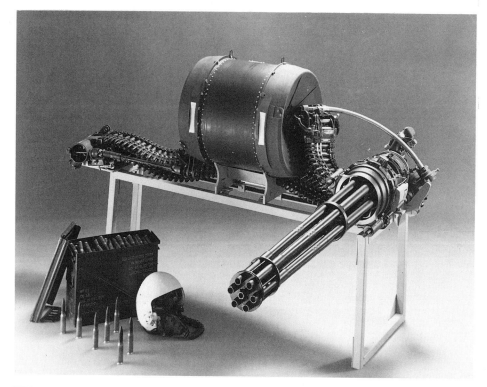

### M61A1 location

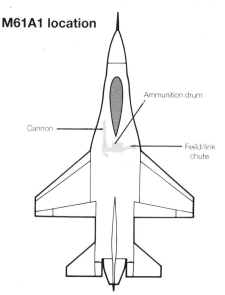

Ammunition drum

Cannon

Feed/link chute

## Wing configurations

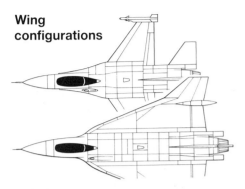

**Above: The far greater surface area of the F-16XL's cranked arrow wing (bottom) and longer fuselage are obvious when compared to the plan view of an early F-16A (top).**

**Above: Alternative powerplants such as GE's J79 turbojet and F101 DFE turbofan have been tested in F-16s.**

**Below: A radical derivative, the large F-16XL could carry twice the payload of a standard F-16.**

## SPECIFICATION

### General Dynamics F-16C (F110-GE-100)

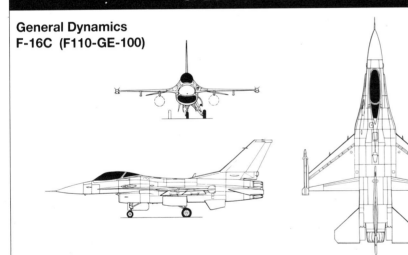

**Dimensions**
Length: 49ft 4in (15.04m)
Height: 16ft 8½in (5.10m)
Wing span: 32ft 9¾in (10.00m)
Tailplane span: 18ft 3¾in (5.58m)
Gross wing area: 300sq ft (27.87m²)

**Weights**
Empty: 19,100lb (8,671kg)
Maximum take-off weight: 42,300lb (19,204kg)
Maximum external load: 12,000lb (5,448kg)

**Power**
1 × General Electric F110-GE-100 afterburning turbofan engine

Maximum thrust: 27,600lb (122.8kN)
Internal fuel: 6,972lb (3,165kg)
External fuel: 6,760lb (3,066kg)

**Performance**
Maximum level speed, high-level: +Mach 2.0 (1,320mph 2,124km/h)
Service ceiling: +50,000ft (15,250m)
Ferry range, with drop tanks: +2,415 miles (3,890km)
Radius of action: +575 miles (925km)

The USAF has also been hard at work, its research programme being based around the rebuilding of its experimental Advanced Fighter Technology Integration F-16 (AFTI/F-16) technology demonstrator. The USAF trials programme, using this aircraft as a flying test-bed, will focus on tests of EO sensors such as a laser

# Developing the Breed

**Above: A highly-modified Fighting Falcon, the AFTI/F-16 sports canard foreplanes and a prominent spine.**

spot tracker, an automatic targeting hand-off system (from aircraft to aircraft, or aircraft to ground station), and an ejection-safe helmet-mounted display linked to a head-steered forward-looking infra-red (FLIR) sensor.

Whether the USAF gets the go-ahead to procure a ground attack version of the Fighting Falcon remains to be seen. What is much more likely to appear in USAF service during the 1990s is the RF-16C: a tactical reconnaissance variant designed to replace the existing force of McDonnell Douglas RF-4C Phantom IIs. In fact, a tactical recce capability for the F-16 has been in service since the early 1980s, when the Dutch started using various European sensor pods on front-line aircraft which were known as F-16A(R)s.

During 1986, GD used an F-16B to successfully flight-test a semi-conformal centreline sensor pod designed by the company. The pod can house a variety of EO/IR sensors to enable both day or night recce operations, providing real-time viewing in the cockpit and near-real-time analysis on the ground. Just what operational configurations will be used remains to be seen, but the RF-16C should start to enter front-line service during the mid-1990s.

In 1988, the US asked Belgium, Denmark, the Netherlands and Norway to join in a two-year pre-development work programme aimed at producing an MSIP IV successor to the F-16C/D. To be known as Agile Falcon, the most obvious difference on the new aircraft

would be a new wing of all-composite construction. The span would be increased from 30ft to 36ft (9.15m to 10.98m), and the chord increased to provide an additional 100sq ft (9.29m$^2$) of wing area. A new wing leading-edge would be swept at 38deg rather than the existing 40deg, and would blend into a larger, more refined LERX. Two additional hardpoints, one under each wing, would also be provided to increase the overall stores capacity.

A redesigned centre fuselage section would be incorporated, giving the Agile Falcon an overall length of 50ft 7in (15.43m), compared to the 49ft 4in (15.04m) of the F-16C. Better avionics and an uprated powerplant would also have been incorporated.

The proposal did attract a degree of interest from some NATO F-16 operators - Turkey hoped to build the aircraft at its Murted aircraft factory - but unfortunately the project was cancelled during 1989 by US Defense Secretary Richard Cheney.

Although termination of Agile Falcon was a blow for General Dynamics, another of the United States' allies is set to produce a derivative of the F-16 during the 1990s. In 1987, Japan announced that the replacement for the Japan Air Self-Defence Force's (JASDF) Mitsubishi F-1 strike aircraft would be derived from either the F-16 Fighting Falcon or the McDonnell Douglas F-15 Eagle (the latter already in service with the JASDF). The chosen airframe would be fitted with selected items of Japanese technology, such as a phased-array radar and an all-new fire control system (FCS).

Knowing that the JASDF favoured a twin-engined model, GD had proposed a

**Above: The wide-angle HUD devised for the AFTI/F-16 forms the basis of the F-16C's HUD unit.**

design known as the FS-X. Derived from the F-16, this would be powered by two GE F404 or P&W PW1120 engines. In practice, the Japanese finally opted for a single-engined aircraft similar to the big-winged Agile Falcon then being proposed to NATO air arms. To be known as

**Below: Heavy emphasis on the use of digital display units is readily apparent in this view of the high-tech AFTI/F-16's cockpit layout.**

**Above: Demonstrating the F-16's versatility, this aircraft carries a centreline reconnaissance pod.**

the SX-3, the aircraft would feature advanced technology composite materials in the forward and aft fuselage sections and in the increased-span wings, while also incorporating Japanese-developed "stealth" technology.

When the decision to adopt the GD proposal was announced, it attracted criticism from within the US and Japanese aerospace industries. The latter (and the JASDF) had favoured an FS-X of indigenous design, and claimed that a US design had been selected for political reasons, namely to reduce the US trade deficit with Japan.

## SX-3 CONTROVERSY

In the US, critics of the decision claimed that Japan was being given access to valuable US technology which might be used at a later date to help Japan compete head-to-head with the US in future aerospace markets. Parallels were drawn with Japan's dominance in other areas of technology, while others warned that US technology might be illegally passed on to the Soviet Union.

The deal eventually hammered out specifies that GD will build one of the

SX-3 prototypes and will receive 40 per cent of the production work; that the aircraft's F100 powerplant will be built in the US; and that the US will have full access to all new SX-3 technology.

Although still recognizable as an F-16, only some 20 to 30 per cent of the airframe will remain unchanged. New features will include a stretched aft fuselage, longer-span wings, vertical canards beneath the engine air inlet, and a strengthened canopy.

**Below: The shape of things to come: Mitsubishi is set to manufacture the advanced technology SX-3 strike aircraft during the 1990s.**

Japanese-developed radar-absorbent materials (RAM) will be used to reduce the overall radar signature, the entire wing leading-edge featuring such materials to help reduce the aircraft's front-sector radar cross-section (RCS)

The avionics suite is being developed by Mitsubishi Electric, Fujitsu and NECA, and will include a control-configured vehicle (CCV)-type FCS offering fully-decoupled flight modes. The SX-3's radar will be an active phased-array unit capable of switching rapidly between air-to-air and air-to-ground modes, while the navaid will be a new inertial navigation system (INS), perhaps combined with a GPS satellite-navigation receiver. An integrated EW system will also be carried.

Provision will be made for the carriage of several types of home-grown weapons, including Mitsubishi's Type 80 ASM and AAM-3 agile air-to-air missile.

If the prototype SX-3 flies on schedule in 1993, production deliveries to the JASDF should begin during 1997. Under present plans, a total of 130 aircraft (though possibly up to 170) will be built by the year 2001 at a predicted cost of $35 million per aircraft. By the time the programme ends, Japan is likely to have paid out some $7 billion in research, development and production costs for this highly controversial "Super F-16".

So what is it like to fly the world's "hottest" small fighter? One of the USAF pilots who flight-tested the YF-16 put it this way: "It's like riding on top of a telegraph pole: every time you light the afterburner, you're a little nervous that it's going to run out from under you." That high acceleration was the result of packing 23,770lb (10,780kg) of thrust into an aircraft weighing less than ten tons in a lightly-loaded (full internal fuel plus two AIM-9 Sidewinder AAMs) take-off configuration. Thrust-to-weight ratio in this condition was a highly impressive 1.1:1.

**Below: Though the F-16 is a single-engined fighter, it gets a powerful "kick" from the afterburning F100 turbofan engine. The engine exhaust nozzle is fully variable.**

Another measurement helping to explain the aircraft's excellent manoeuvrability is its wing loading. In designing the F-16, GD calculated that the optimum wing loading would be around 68lb/sq ft (331kg/m$^2$), but aimed for a lower weight of 60lb/sq ft (293kg/m$^2$). This was to allow for the inevitable increase in weight of a production aircraft, as well as helping to maximize the aircraft's rate of turn at subsonic speeds.

The subsequent increase in weight of the production F-16A did indeed degrade the original figures: wing loading rose to 81.5lb/sq ft (398kg/m$^2$), resulting in a lightly-loaded take-off thrust-to-weight ratio of 0.97:1. Despite this fall in performance, the F-16A's figures were still superior to those of its contemporaries: the wing loading of a MiG-21 Fishbed is

around 85lb/sq ft (415kg/m$^2$), while that of a Dassault Mirage F.1E is around 120lb/sq ft (585kg/m$^2$).

The F-16C is some 1,950lb (884kg) heavier than the A-model, producing wing loading and thrust-to-weight figures for an F100-powered aircraft of 88.21lb/sq ft (430kg/m$^2$) and 0.90:1 respectively. The F110-powered F-16C is even heavier, so its wing loading is 90.81lb/sq ft (443kg/m$^2$), but the increased thrust of the General Electric (GE) powerplant boosts the thrust-to-weight ratio up to 1.06:1 – a figure close to that originally planned for the F-16A Fighting Falcon.

Fit an F110 turbofan into an F-16A, and the wing loading will rise by an extra 2lb/sq ft (9.76kg/m$^2$) as a result of the GE engine's additional 693lb (314kg) of weight; but the thrust-to-weight ratio will

**Left: An excellent illustration of the strong LERX-generated vortexes produced when the F-16 is flown in tight manoeuvres. The vortexes help improve airflow over the wings.**

Falcon's mission. There are, however, two notable exceptions: when the cover door for the spine-mounted air refuelling receptacle is opened, response in pitch and roll is reduced somewhat to make the aircraft more docile during the critical refuelling phase; and when the undercarriage is lowered, the FBW/FCS gain is reduced by some 50 per cent.

In addition to "taming" the F-16's relaxed stability, the FBW/FCS also ensures that the pilot cannot over-stress the airframe during high-g air-combat manoeuvring. No matter how hard the pilot operates the controls, the system will keep the AoA below 25deg and the load factor below 9g.

Block 30 F-16s were cleared to pull 9g combat manoeuvres at weights of just over 26,000lb (11,791kg). With the Block 40/42 aircraft, this figure rose to 28,500lb (12,925kg), and this will increase further to 29,500lb (13,378kg) on Block 50/52 F-16C/Ds. However, the 9g manoeuvring capability is not available under all operating conditions, but depends on a combination of factors such as altitude, Mach number and aircraft weight.

rise to a very impressive 1.15:1. Several nations are known to be interested in just such an airframe-powerplant combination, but it is is unlikely to appear for at least two reasons: 1) any such aircraft would have to be fitted with a larger air inlet to meet the airflow demands of the F110 powerplant; 2) any such aircraft would be able to outfly most USAF F-16s!

Future plans envisage even more power being available when the 29,000lb (13,152 kg) thrust F110-GE-129 and F100-PW-229 engines become operational during the early-1990s.

### PILOT-FRIENDLY

Two features play an important part in giving the Fighting Falcon its vice-free handling characteristics: the variable-camber wing and the LERX. As flight conditions change, the wing leading-edge manoeuvring flaps and trailing-edge flaperons can be deflected up to 35deg/sec by the FCS to match the aircraft's

speed and AoA. This helps reduce drag and maintain lift at high AoA. Vortexes generated by the LERX improve airflow over the wings and vertical tail, thus enhancing lift, pitch and directional stability, particularly at high AoA.

The FBW/FCS remains at full gain throughout the majority of the Fighting

**Below: Without its electronic fly-by-wire system, the F-16 would not be controllable.**

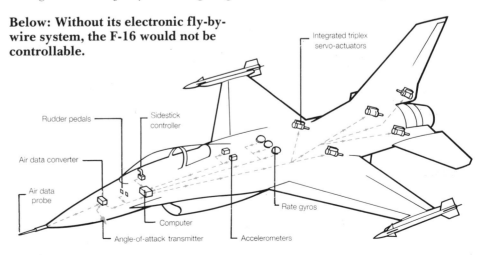

Rudder pedals

Sidestick controller

Air data converter

Air data probe

Angle-of-attack transmitter

Computer

Accelerometers

Rate gyros

Integrated triplex servo-actuators

# Combat Capabilities

Let's take the case of an F-16C carrying a half-load of internal fuel, two wingtip-mounted AIM-9 Sidewinders and 511 rounds of 20mm ammunition for the M61 gun. In order to achieve 9g of instantaneous manoeuvrability, the aircraft must be flying faster than Mach 0.6 at low level. As operating altitude rises, more speed is needed: around Mach 0.75 at 10,000ft (3,050m); more than Mach 0.9 at 20,000ft (6,100m); and Mach 1.2 at 30,000ft (9,150m). Above this last height, 9g manoeuvring is virtually ruled out. Speeds above Mach 1.2 can even produce a slight decrease in manoeuvrability, until a steady but small increase starts again at around Mach 1.4.

Speeds of around Mach 1.2 offer the best instantaneous manoeuvring capability: 9g at 30,000ft (9,150m); 7g at up to 32,000ft (9,760m); 5g at around 44,000ft (13,420m); and 3g at up to 55,000ft (16,775m).

If such hard manoeuvring is to be sustained for more than the briefest of periods, the restrictions become even more severe as 9g can be obtained and held in only a narrow "corridor" of altitude and speed combinations. At low level, this speed range is between Mach 0.75 and 0.95. Climb a few thousand feet, and the lower speed creeps up to around Mach 0.8/0.85. At 10,000ft (3,050m) or above, sustained 9g manoeuvring is out of the question.

**Left: With easy access via a starboard panel, up to 500 rounds of 20mm belt-fed cannon ammunition can be loaded into the magazine.**

**Below: Trailing a plume of smoke as the six-barrel M61A1 bursts into life, an F-16A rips apart a ground target with its gunfire.**

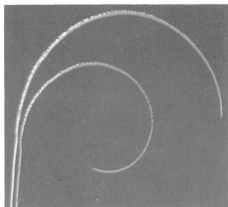

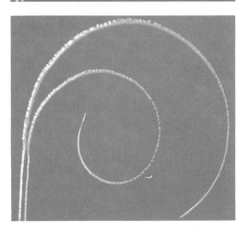

For sustained manoeuvring at 5g or more, the Fighting Falcon is restricted to a speed bracket of between Mach 0.5 and 1.1 at sea level, rising to between Mach 0.8 and 1.3 at 20,000ft (6,100m).

## TIGHT TURNS

The F-16 is most definitely not an aircraft to tangle with in a dogfight. A measure of its superior turning performance came during flight-testing of the YF-16 in a 325-350kt turn against an F-4 Phantom II. In the time it took the former to complete a 360deg turn, the bigger F-4 could only manage some 240 to 250deg.

Reference books often quote impressive range figures for combat aircraft, but these must be interpreted carefully. A given figure for "maximum range" is probably the maximum distance that the aircraft can fly under optimum cruise conditions. It may also assume the use of external fuel tanks, and may ignore the effects of weather or the need for realistic fuel reserves. A more reliable figure is that given for the aircraft's ferry range, as this indicates the maximum distance that can be flown on a deployment sortie. In the case of an F-16C carrying external fuel tanks, this latter figure is more than 2,100 nm (3,885km).

Determining the useful combat radius is not simply a matter of dividing that figure by two (outbound and homebound) and deducting a little bit for luck. On a maximum ferry range mission, the F-16 is more than likely going to carry the maximum number of external fuel tanks, and the pilot will be careful not to depart from optimum cruise conditions. However, a pilot on a combat mission will have ordnance on some (or even all) of the hardpoints, and must plan for fuel-saving manoeuvres when he engages the enemy.

An F100 turbofan engine running at full military (non-afterburning) power burns approximately 170lb (77kg) of precious fuel per minute. Engage full afterburner, and that figure will at least quadruple.

A typical F-16 air-to-air combat mission may well see the aircraft armed with two wingtip-mounted AIM-9 Sidewinders and an AIM-7 Sparrow on each outboard underwing hardpoint. Clipping weapons on every hardpoint might sound good, but in the real world of combat the F-16's F100/F110 turbofan needs enough fuel to guarantee adequate mission endurance. More often than not, this results in a 370 US gal (1,400 litre) external fuel tank being carried on each inboard underwing hardpoint, along with a 300 US gal (1,135 litre) tank on the under-fuselage centreline hardpoint.

It is impossible to predict the demands of combat at the mission planning stage, but a realistic allowance might be to assume that while flying at maximum power setting at 15,000ft (4,575m), the F-16 will be required to accelerate from Mach 0.8 to Mach 1.2, pulling five 360deg turns at the lower speed.

**Weapon loads**

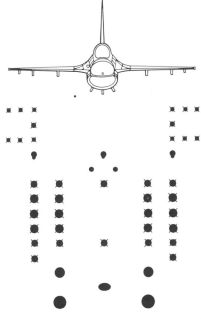

**Above: Clearly demonstrating its far superior turning capabilities, a Fighting Falcon (inner track) out-loops the bigger and heavier F-4 Phantom II with apparent ease.**

**Right: Though smaller and lighter than most of its counterparts, the F-16 can carry a wide range of ordnance on six underwing, two wingtip and one centreline weapon stations.**

# Combat Capabilities

**Left: In addition to the underwing and wingtip weapon stations, an underfuselage centreline station can be used. In this case, it is carrying an ALQ-119 ECM pod.**

Fuel provisions also have to take into account pre-take-off consumption, allowing for, say, ten minutes of engine running at flight-idle during the time it takes from engine-start to the beginning of the take-off run. The take-off run and build-up of speed to around 300kts will then require the engine to run at maximum power, and will probably be followed by a climb to the optimum cruising altitude on full military (non-afterburning) power.

On return to base, further allowances must be made for landing, plus any hitches en route. For instance, the aircraft may be delayed by bad weather or navigational error; or it may have to loiter at low altitude near to base before being allowed to land. A realistic fuel allowance to cover such eventualities would be enough to safely allow a 20-minute loiter at low altitude.

Finally, a fuel allowance may have to be made for loitering on station. An air-defence fighter despatched to intercept an intruder is pretty well guaranteed to find the target appearing on time and close to the predicted intercept point (IP); but a fighter flying an air-superiority mission must actually linger in the airspace it is trying to defend. Tactical radius is thus very dependant on the F-16's required time on station.

Taking the aircraft loading conditions and fuel allowances listed above, the tactical radius of the F-16C works out at around 740nm (1,369km) with no loiter at maximum range. Half an hour of loitering cuts this figure to just over 600nm (1,110 km); while an hour of combat air patrol (CAP) brings the tactical radius down still further to 500nm (925km). A two-hour CAP mission is possible at ranges of just over 250nm (462km).

Those 370 US gal (1,400 litre) underwing fuel tanks play an important part in

If most of the flight has to be made through airspace contested by the enemy, the mission profile becomes "Lo-Lo-Lo": the pilot has no option but to fly the entire route at low level and accept the increased fuel consumption this involves.

## COMBAT LOADINGS

To see the effect of this, let's take an F-16C configured for an air defence mission, but replace the two AIM-7 Sparrows with a pair of 2,000lb (907kg) Mk 84 bombs for a Hi-Lo-Hi strike mission. Fuel reserves for take-off and landing will remain unchanged, and the combat phase of the mission will be assumed to comprise a 50nm (92.5km) dash to and from the target in full dry thrust, at speeds of 565 to 600kts true air speed (KTAS).

**Below: With practice bombs on the underwing racks, an F-16C hurtles over the desert on a high-speed, low-level training exercise. Note the large 300 US gal (1,136 litre) fuel tank on the centreline station.**

**Above: Caught in a shallow dive towards the target area, an F-16 releases six Mk 82 500lb (227kg) free-fall, high-explosive bombs from its underwing racks.**

extending the F-16's mission endurance. Leave them off, and the one-hour CAP range falls dramatically to only 200nm (370km), and the maximum tactical range is cut to not much more than 400nm (740km)

On F-16 strike missions, another factor comes into play: cruise height. If the aircraft is operating under conditions of air superiority, or is attacking targets close to the front line, it may be able to fly most of the way to and from the target area at the most fuel-efficient combination of speed and height, only descending to low level for the final dash to and from the target area. This sort of mission profile is known as "Hi-Lo-Hi".

# Combat Capabilities

Tactical range under such conditions works out at 770nm (1,424km), assuming that the pilot is permitted to jettison his three external fuel tanks once they have been emptied. If these high-drag stores have to be retained for the entire mission, the tactical radius falls to 650nm (1,202 km) Should the two underwing tanks be swapped for an extra pair of Mk 84 bombs, these figures fall to 370nm (684km) and 345nm (638km) respectively.

If the mission has to be flown Lo-Lo-Lo, these range figures are further reduced by up to 45 per cent. The F-16C with two Mk 84 bombs and three external fuel tanks will have a range of approximately 420nm (777km), or 370nm (684km) if the empty tanks have to be retained. For the aircraft carrying four Mk 84s and only the centreline fuel tank, range falls to 235nm (434km) and 225nm (416km) respectively.

Moving on from the facts and figures, how does the pilot's "office" rate when it comes to combat? A big plus over many of its contemporaries is the superb all-round view provided by the Fighting Falcon's bubble canopy. This allows the pilot to "check his six" for enemy fighters, as well as allowing him to make sure that he's not generating a contrail which might

Above: Taxying out prior to the start of a mission, this close-up of the F-16 bubble canopy reveals its frameless configuration. Also clearly evident is the 30deg rearward tilt of the pilot's ejection seat.

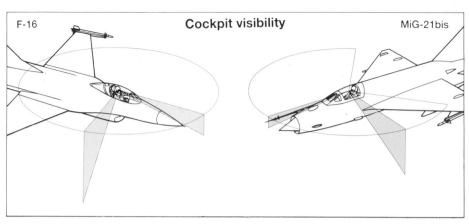

F-16    Cockpit visibility    MiG-21bis

Above: The F-16's frameless bubble canopy provides the pilot with an excellent all-round field of view. In contrast, the MiG-21bis pilot has inferior forward vision and a significant rear "blind spot".

betray his position. The view downwards is almost as good, and a small amount of bank will allow the pilot to look vertically downwards.

One novel problem is that the one-piece transparency has no canopy frame(s), and pilots instinctively use such features in their forward field-of-view as reference points when trying to position the horizon during normal flight. Pilots new to the F-16 are thus recommended to fly by instruments until they become accustomed to the novel external view.

## HOTAS ADVANTAGE

In combat, the pilot's main target-detection sensor is, of course, the aircraft's radar. In the F-16, this has been designed for ease-of-use during combat; indeed, the F-16 was probably the first aircraft in service to apply the hands-on-throttle-and-stick (HOTAS) principle, whereby all of the controls needed during air combat are mounted on the throttle and flight control "stick".

On the F-16A/B, the radar fitted was the Westinghouse APG-66: a pulse-doppler set offering air-to-air and air-to-ground modes, as well as the ability to look up or down to track high- or low-flying targets. Both these modes may be

selected by the pilot using the throttle, side-stick control or radar control panel. During air-to-ground missions, the radar can provide improved-resolution images of ground targets by use of expanded display and doppler beam sharpening.

The F-16C/D sports the improved Westinghouse APG-68 radar which uses new dual-mode tube technology to deliver more transmitted power during air-to-air combat, plus a programmable signal processor (PSP). That extra power results in longer-range tactical modes and the ability to fire radar-guided AAMs at beyond visual range (BVR) targets; while the improved data processing allows the APG-68 to track multiple targets, detect surface vessels, and provide high-resolution mapping modes.

In air-to-air combat, three of the radar's most useful features are: track-while-scan (TWS); raid cluster resolution (RCR); and air combat manoeuvring (ACM) modes. The first allows the radar to maintain tracks of several high-priority targets while continuing to search for others; the second allows the pilot to distinguish between individual aircraft detected in a tight formation at long range; and the third mode allows the radar to follow hard-manoeuvring targets flying at relatively close range.

The LANTIRN HUD on Block 40/42 aircraft combines traditional HUD symbology with a raster-scanned (TV-style) display of imagery from the EO system. In air-to-air combat, this HUD can act as a simple lead-computing optical sight (LCOS) and an expanded-envelope gun sight (EEGS), as well as providing snapshoot and AIM-9 Sidewinder slaving.

A small control panel located just below the combiner glass (and thus

**Below: The EO pods used as part of the LANTIRN system are carried on cheek-mounted stations, either side of the engine intake. The LANTIRN system allows the F-16 to undertake a wider range of mission profiles.**

within the pilot's peripheral field-of-vision) provides the pilot with most of the controls he will need in combat. Using this, he can feed data into the aircraft's FCS, control the FLIR, and change radio channels or IFF modes.

As their title suggests, the two multi-function cathode-ray tube (CRT) display screens can be configured to meet the tactical needs of the moment. For example, they can display the fire-control or terrain-following radar (TFR) information – including high-resolution radar pictures – or imagery from the navigation or targetting EO sensor pods. Other possible modes include AGM-65 Maverick AGM aiming and an indication of overall weapon status.

Unlike the main radar, the Rockwell-supplied GPS satellite-navigation unit is entirely passive, thus denying the enemy any clues of an imminent attack. Signals broadcast from a network of navigation satellites provide the precise all-weather position information required if the F-16 is to fly at low level and deliver precise attacks on specific targets.

Signals from the satellites can, however, be received by friend and foe alike, and equipment to receive them, albeit with only a medium level of accuracy, is commercially available. Military users need far more accurate data which is encrypted into the radio signal, thus making it theoretically available to only the US and its Western allies.

THE modern jet fighter is a highly complex item of hardware, and reliability is just as important an aspect of its overall performance as speed and combat ceiling. No matter how impressive the specification of a warplane might appear on paper, the fact is that such information isn't worth the paper it is written on if the aircraft isn't available on demand. Yet figures on the reliability of a warplane are not the sort of thing you will find in most reference books; and it's easy to draw the conclusion that many aircraft manufacturers and operators would probably like to keep it that way.

In the case of the F-16, things are somewhat different. Every year, GD compiles the statistics covering recent F-16 operations, and prints the data in a declassified briefing book which makes unspectacular but interesting reading. In short, the figures quoted for the Fighting Falcon are enough to make most Air Force commanders drool with envy.

**Above: Primed and readied, a pair of 50th TFW F-16Cs wait to take to the air again. Relatively easy to maintain, the F-16 has proved to be a highly reliable aircraft.**

Right from the start, the Fighting Falcon proved to be a very reliable aircraft in both USAF and NATO service. By 1980 it was exceeding the former's Tactical Air Command (TAC) standard for mission capability – the number of aircraft completely or partly mission-capable – of 70 per cent by an average of four to six points, making it the most reliable fighter in US service. Similar figures were reported by NATO users: within two years of taking delivery of its first F-16As, the Belgian Air Force (the first NATO operator) was reporting an availability rate of no less than 88 per cent.

In 1987 and 1988, USAF F-16 fleet readiness was around 90 per cent, while sortie surge exercises had demonstrated typical sortie rates of 4.5 to 6.5 sorties per day, the record being 8 sorties in a 12-hour period. Indeed, units reported that sortie surge rates were being limited by pilot availability, not by the aircraft.

**Left: Signing the flight release form, an 8th TFW pilot clears the last administrative hurdle before the start of another mission. Note the large underwing fuel tank.**

Maintenance man-hours for all models averaged out at around 10 hours per flying hour, with figures for the later C/D models proving consistently better than those for the A/B models. The figure of 10 hours is impressive – during the 1960s, many air forces had maintenance man-hour figures averaging 100 or more per flying hour.

Several factors have combined to make the F-16 more reliable. Talk to anyone who maintained a first-generation Mach 2 fighter, and you will hear some real "horror stories" about access to some notoriously unreliable sub-systems requiring major "surgery" such as removal of the ejection seat, or even an engine.

When aircraft such as the F-16 were designed, this sort of design mis-feature just wasn't allowed. More than 250 access covers or doors on the Fighting Falcon airframe allow ground crew to work on the aircraft's innards, and more than 60

**Above: From the outset, the F-16 was designed with easy maintenance in mind. The majority of the aircraft's access panels can be worked on from ground level.**

per cent of the airframe's external surface is removable. Around 90 per cent of the components are accessible from ground level, with only five per cent located behind other components. Others are designed to be interchangeable between port and starboard, including large assemblies such as the stabilators, wing flaperons, smaller components including most parts making up the main landing gear, and many actuator units.

So much for the theory. The practical test for any fighter is combat, and for the F-16 that came in spectacular fashion on 7 June 1981 when eight Israeli F-16As carried out a daring Hi-Lo-Hi strike against the Osarik nuclear reactor which Iraq had built at Twartha, near Baghdad. Israeli intelligence services believed that the Osarik plant would be used to manufacture plutonium, thus allowing Iraq to develop nuclear weapons. This was a risk which Israel could not accept, and the

decision was taken to destroy Osarik.

The Israel Defence Force/Air Force (IDF/AF) timed its 7 June raid so as to catch the reactor in an almost-completed state, but before it had actually started operating. A strike after the reactor had "gone critical" would have released a cloud of intensely radioactive material into the atmosphere.

Although the F-16 had been in IDF/AF service for only 14 months (53 had been delivered against an order for 75 aircraft), it was selected for the mission. Its long endurance provided the range needed for

the flight to and from Twartha, while its ground-mapping radar modes and accurate navigation/attack systems gave a high chance of success.

The eight F-16As used were each armed with two 2,000lb (907kg) Mk 84 "iron" bombs and two underwing external drop tanks, and were escorted to and from the target by six F-15A Eagles. In the early hours of Sunday 7 June, the force took off, probably form Etzion air base, near Eilat. Many details of the mission have never been released, but the outbound flight probably took them across southern Jordan and the desolate northern part of Saudi Arabia, before turning northwards into Iraqi airspace.

## TARGET APPROACH

Briefly fired on by anti-aircraft (AA) batteries as they crossed the Iraqi border, the attackers reached the target area at around 6.30am local time. Approaching

**Below: An Israeli F-16, suitably loaded with bombs, missiles and fuel tanks. Bomb-carrying F-16As were used in the Israeli attack on the Iraqi nuclear plant at Osarik.**

# Front-line Operations

from the west, the F-16s attacked in two waves, each consisting of two pairs of aircraft. Despite detection at the Iraqi border, the attackers achieved complete surprise, and they faced only AA fire rather than the surface-to-air missiles (SAMs) which were believed to defend the Iraqi site.

Pressing home their attack, the first wave of F-16s scored at least two hits on the concrete cupola covering the reactor. This collapsed, badly damaging the reactor itself and burying it in rubble. Unchallenged by Iraqi fighters – each bomb run had taken less than two minutes – the F-16s and their F-15 escorts then flew westwards, back across Jordan and then into Israeli airspace.

Having proved itself in the tactical bombing role, the F-16 was soon to pass the ultimate test of any fighter – air-to-air combat. Again it was the IDF/AF which put its Fighting Falcons to good use, this time clashing with the Syrian Air Force in the skies over southern Lebanon during the battles of 1982.

As Israeli ground forces pushed north on 6 June to begin Operation "Peace for

**Below: There is no doubt that the MiG-29 Fulcrum is a very capable fighter, but many believe the F-16 still has a winning edge.**

Galilee" – the invasion and occupation of southern Lebanon – IDF/AF fighters were on hand to deal with Syrian fighters. The first air combat was reported on 8 June, but the action didn't hot up until the following afternoon when the Israelis began a crippling series of attacks on Syrian air-defence SAM batteries located in the Bekaa Valley. More than 60 MiG-21 Fishbeds and -23 Floggers joined the air battle, and the IDF/AF claimed the destruction of 29 Syrian fighters by its F-15 and F-16 units. Further clashes in the following days saw this figure rise to more than 80 claimed "kills".

Following a short-lived ceasefire, the two air forces were in combat again from 24 June onwards, and by the end of the summer Israel claimed to have destroyed 93 Syrian fighters. More than half of these were MiG-23s, the remainder being mainly MiG-21s and Sukhoi Su-22s. Of the total, 44 had fallen to F-16s and 40 to F-15s.

The Israelis attributed part of their success to poor enemy tactics, claiming that Syrian pilots rushed into combat, showing little evidence of pre-flight planning. As an unidentified senior Israeli officer put it: ". . . they could have flown the best fighter in the world, but if they flew the way they were flying, we would have shot them down. It wasn't the equipment at fault, but their tactics . . .

They fired missiles, they fought, but in a peculiar way . . . in our opinion, they acted without tactical sense."

Much less publicity has been given to the combat successes of F-16s operated by the Pakistan Air Force (PAF), which have occurred as a result of the war in Afghanistan. When the Soviet-equipped Afghan Air Force began to violate Pakistani airspace to bomb refugee camps during the second half of the 1980s, PAF F-16s were given the task of repelling them, and press reports from the area have claimed that at least four Afghan fighter-bombers have been brought down with AIM-9 Sidewinder AAMs as a result. Statistics published by GD in May 1989 credited the PAF F-16s with 16 "kills" for no losses, although the loss of at least one Fighting Falcon during a combat mission has been reported in the Western press.

## MiG ADVERSARIES

Should the F-16 be called upon to participate in any air battles during the 1990s, whether in the Middle East or elsewhere, its most likely adversary will not be the MiG-21 or -23, but the highly potent MiG-29 Fulcrum. In the spirit of glasnost, examples of the Fulcrum have been displayed to great effect at airshows in the West, but this author still believes that,

**Above: Almost all F-16s carry a pair of AIM-9 Sidewinder AAMs on the wingtip launch rails as part of their air defence armament.**

when it comes to combat manoeuvres, the F-16 is ahead of the (larger) Soviet fighter, particularly in its roll rate.

The appearance of the MiG-29 in the West also allowed GD to make a video tape comparing the show routines of the F-16C, MiG-29, the multi-national European Fighter Aircraft (EFA), and the Dassault-Breguet Rafale. A split-screen presentation of the results showed all four aircraft flying the same manoeuvres, and it was clear that although the performance of the F-16C was bettered by one of the other aircraft under some conditions, for most of the time it clearly outflew its airshow rivals.

When it comes to armament for air-to-air combat, the MiG-29's ability to carry AA-10 Archer AAMs is a bonus, as is the use of a laser ranger/designator. However, when the AIM-120A AMRAAM eventually enters service, F-16 pilots should be at a distinct advantage. In air-to-air combat, the F-16's smaller size, more modern avionics, "pilot-friendly" cockpit, and (to my mind) better agility should give it the edge over the MiG fighter.

All current F-16 operators are equipped with AIM-9 Sidewinders, but not all users are cleared to receive the AIM-9L. Two export models of the Sidewinder – the AIM-9P-3 and the newer, all-aspect AIM-9P-4 – are available to these operators, as are several non-US missiles. Qualification firings of the French Matra

R.530 Magic 2 from the F-16 began in May 1989, with a standard operational load of one on each wingtip rail and two on underwing hardpoints envisaged. Successful integration trials with the F-16 and the Rafael Python 3 were also conducted during 1989, an adaptor allowing the Israeli AAM to be mounted on Sidewinder launch rails.

Strike missions will be made easier – at least for the USAF – by the recent deployment of LANTIRN equipment. Having this system on F-16s based in West Germany allows the aircraft to operate over a 16-hour "window" in mid-winter, instead of the previous 4.5 hours.

During a typical night attack, the F-16 would make its initial approach using automatic terrain-following. The pilot's HUD would be used to display a FLIR image, plus superimposed terrain-following commands and navigation/flight parameters. One of the pilot's two head-down multifunction displays, used in conjunction with the terrain-following radar (TFR) in the navigation pod, would show an "E-scope" display and provide control functions.

Once close to the target, the F-16 would fly a pop-up manoeuvre for target acquisition. To assist the pilot, the HUD would show FLIR imagery of the terrain ahead of the aircraft, superimposing target-

cueing symbols derived from radar and inertial navigation system (INS) data. The final attack would be visual, with the pilot breaking away from the target area after weapon release and rapidly taking the F-16 back to the relative safety of low-level terrain-following flight.

By day, the LANTIRN targeting pod could be used to control laser-guided bombs (LGB) such as the GBU-10. Once the target has been acquired by radar using one of the high-resolution modes, it is accurately aligned with the radar cursor, and cueing information is sent to the targeting pod. Using the pod's EO and IR systems, a typical LGB target such as a bridge should be acquired at ranges up to 15nm (27.7km) The pilot then flies a loft-bombing manoeuvre, pulling around 4g and releasing the bomb at up to 6nm (11km) from the target. The pilot can fly an evasive manoeuvre to avoid enemy air defences, safe in the knowledge that the pod autotracker will keep the target illuminated with laser energy so that the LGB can home accurately. At no time will the F-16 approach be closer than 3nm (5.5km) from the target.

**Below: The LANTIRN targeting pod allows the F-16 to use laser-guided bombs, four of which are loaded on this Fighting Falcon.**

THE largest Fighting Falcon fleet is that of the USAF, with 785 F-16A/Bs and over 700 F-16C/Ds delivered by early-1990. The service is also committed to the purchase of a further 381 F-16s, and by the time production finally comes to an end, the USAF is likely to have taken delivery of some 3,000 F-16s.

The USAF accepted its first production F-16A on 17 August 1978, but it was to be another two years before the first F-16-equipped Tactical Fighter Squadron (TFS) achieved Initial Operating Capability (IOC). The training unit for both USAF and export customers was Tactical Air Command's (TAC) 388th Tactical Fighter Wing (TFW) at Hill Air Force Base, Utah. The Wing received its first Fighting Falcon in January 1979 and reached its full operating strength of 102 aircraft by the end of that year. This allowed IOC of one of the Wing's squadrons – the 4th TFS – to be declared by TAC on 12 November 1980.

**Below: A busy flightline at Hill AFB, Utah, with 388th TFW F-16s being prepared for another round of pilot training sorties.**

The first overseas deployment of USAF F-16s came in March 1981, when 12 388th TFW aircraft were sent to Flesland in Norway for a month, with seven aircraft returning to Europe in June 1981 to win the Royal Air Force-sponsored tactical bombing competition at the first attempt. That same summer also saw the first deliveries of F-16s to the 8th TFW. Based at Kunsan Air Base (AB) in South Korea, the Wing (nicknamed the "Wolf Pack") forms part of the USAF's Pacific Air Forces (PACAF).

## PRINCIPAL ROLE

By the time production of the F-16A/B had ended in early 1985, the USAF had taken delivery of 785 such aircraft, and all but 50 or so were still in service in early 1990. The Fighting Falcon is now the

**Above: Excellent close-formation flying by a quartet of 8th TFW "Wolf Pack" F-16s. This PACAF Wing is based in South Korea.**

USAF's main ground attack aircraft, having largely replaced the venerable F-4 Phantom II, and by early-1990 some 1,500 examples had entered service with the USAF.

Air defence of the continental United States (CONUS) is the responsibility of TAC's 1st Air Force, whose 24th and 25th Air Divisions have their headquarters at Griffiss AFB, New York, and McChord AFB, Washington, respectively. By the mid-1980s, the CONUS air defences were badly in need of improvement, with the last dedicated air defence interceptor – the Convair F-106A Delta Dart – having been in service for some 30 years. The surviving examples of the 320 built were now in service with Air National Guard (ANG) units, most of the responsibility for air defence having been taken over by F-4-equipped ANG units. Though younger than the F-106, the F-4 was getting long in the tooth and could not match the pace of Soviet bombers like the Tupolev Tu-22M Backfire.

In the short term, the simplest solution was to assign three F-15-equipped units

**Below: Several ANG squadrons have traded in their F-106A Delta Darts for the F-16A (ADF), including the 119th FIS/New Jersey ANG.**

to the air-defence role, but a cheaper aircraft had to be found to re-equip the ANG's Fighter Interceptor Squadrons (FIS) as soon as possible.

The F-16 had begun to enter ANG service during 1982, initially as a replacement for ageing ground attack aircraft such as the Vought A-7D Corsair II. The problem of selecting a new Air Defence Fighter (ADF) remained unresolved at this time, although Northrop hoped that its private-venture F-20 Tigershark would be selected. However, during 1986, the USAF announced its intention to modify existing F-16As to fill the ADF requirement. Although smaller than the F-4, the F-16 offered longer range and better capabilities against low-signature targets such as "cruise" missiles.

The first ANG unit to deploy the converted F-16A (ADF) was the 114th Tactical Fighter Training Squadron (TFTS), Oregon ANG, which received its first aircraft during 1989. This was followed shortly after by delivery of the first aircraft to the 194th FIS, California ANG. Current plans call for a total of 14 squadrons (a mix of TAC and ANG units) to re-equip with the converted aircraft.

As the F-16A (ADF) has entered service, so another new weapon has made its debut. This is the GPU-5 gun pod, which houses a 30mm rotary cannon firing the same cartridges as those of the Fairchild A-10A Thunderbolt II's GAU-8 multi-barrel gun. The former has a maximum rate of fire of 2,400 rounds per minute, and can be fired on its own or in conjunction with the F-16's integral M61A1 multi-barrel unit. If the ANG trials prove successful, the GPU-5 could be adopted by the USAF for service use.

The Air Force Reserve (AFRes) has been slower to re-equip with the Fighting Falcon, with the first examples not entering its ranks until 1984 when the 466th TFS traded in its Republic F-105 Thunderchiefs. However, it wasn't until 1989 that a further two AFRes units re-equipped with the F-16.

Deployment of the F-16 to European-based units started in December 1982, the recipient being the United States Air Forces in Europe's (USAFE) 50th TFW

**Below: Three squadrons within the 50th TFW at Hahn AB, West Germany, operate the F-16C/D.**

# Fighting Falcon Fliers

at Hahn AB, one of three F-16-equipped USAFE Wings based in West Germany.

In 1987, the German-based 52nd TFW began to deploy Block 30 F-16C/Ds as replacements for their F-4Es. The latter had been used by the Wing as "bomb trucks" to provide extra air-to-ground firepower in support of its relatively small force of F-4G "Wild Weasel" defence-suppression aircraft. The F-16 continues this support role, but the Block 30 aircraft can also carry the AIM-45 Shrike ARM. With the arrival of Block 40 aircraft, the escorting F-16s will also be able to deliver the more effective AGM-88 HARM.

Following the initial deliveries to German-based units, F-16s were delivered to USAFE's Spanish-based 401st TFW during 1983. By 1991, the Wing, its three squadrons and their aircraft will have moved to a new home at Crotone, Italy. That, at least, is the current plan, but nothing can be certain with significant defence cuts and force reductions in the 1990s all but inevitable. A question mark also hangs over the sole F-16 unit to be based in the United Kingdom. Based at Royal Air Force (RAF) Bentwaters,

Suffolk, the 527th Aggressor Squadron (AS) operates a dozen or so F-16s in the dissimilar air combat training (DACT) role, teaching NATO fighter pilots how to get the best of a potential adversary in a dogfight.

In 1987, the F-16 finally joined the US Navy. The service had been interested in the aircraft since the early 1970s, seeing it as a replacement for both the F-4 and A-7 then in service. Such was the Navy's interest that it had gone as far as joining the USAF's LWF programme, but when the latter service selected the YF-16 in 1975, the Navy bowed out, arguing that it needed more time to study all of the rival LWF designs.

Several "navalized" F-16s were subsequently proposed, including a single-seat design which would have used the fuselage of the two-seat trainer model in order to obtain more internal volume for

**Above: Wearing an appropriate code number on its intake, this F-16C adversary trainer is painted in the camouflage colours worn by Eastern Bloc MiG-29 Fulcrums.**

**Below: In complete contrast, the USAF's "Thunderbirds" display team F-16s wear a flamboyant and very patriotic colour scheme. The team has used the F-16 since 1983.**

avionics and fuel. Unfortunately for GD, the Navy was to choose the McDonnell Douglas/Northrop F-18 Hornet to meet its front-line needs.

However, 26 F-16s do serve with the US Navy, the aircraft being built during 1987/88 to serve in the DACT role. Designated F/TF-16N, they are based on the F-16C/D and are powered by the F110-GE-100 turbofan engine. A strengthened wing has been fitted, along with provision for the carriage of air combat manoeuvring instrumentation (ACMI) equipment. No integral cannon is carried, and they retain the APG-86 radar of the F-16A. In addition, their EW fit consists of an ALR-69 RWR and the ALE-40 chaff/flare dispenser.

The initial Navy order was for 22 single-seaters and four two-seat trainers, and IOC was achieved in April 1987 at Naval Air Station (NAS) Miramar, California. In October of the same year, an East coast unit received its first aircraft. Delivery of the 26 aircraft was completed in May 1988, but the Navy now hopes to buy another 26 examples.

The first European air arm to take delivery of the F-16 was the Belgian Air Force, which took delivery of a Gossellies-built example on 29 January 1979. Just under two years later, 349 Squadron was officially assigned to NATO, being declared fully operational on 6 May of the same year.

## BELGIAN DELIVERIES

Delivery of 116 Fighting Falcons (96 single-seaters and 20 two-seaters) to the Belgian Air Force was completed in May 1985, with aircraft completed to Block 10 standard from the 54th example onwards. The older aircraft were progressively rebuilt and updated to this standard in a programme initiated in 1981.

The first of 44 follow-on aircraft was delivered during 1987, these being built to Block 15 OCU configuration and used to replace elderly Dassault-Mirage 5BRs in Belgian service. It had been planned to fit

**Above: The US Navy is a relative newcomer to F-16 operations, with 26 F/TF-16Ns (navalized F-16C/Ds) serving in the DACT role. More examples are likely to be procured.**

part of the F-16 fleet with the LORAN Rapport III EW system (mounted in a tail fairing), but this proved impossible given Belgium's chronic shortage of defence funds and possible problems in transferring the necessary technology from the US. Under a 1989 contract, all Belgian F-16s will now be fitted with the much simpler Electronique Serge Dassault Carpace passive EW system.

Belgium is committed to giving its F-16s a mid-life update which will help them to survive into the early years of the next century. Again, the chronic shortage of funds has forced the cancellation of any plans to procure a replacement fighter until at least then – but if the present high rate of F-16 attrition continues, the Belgian Air Force will have lost all of its F-16s before a replacement enters service!

The Royal Netherlands Air Force accepted its first F-16 on 6 June 1979, the first unit to relinquish its F-104Gs being 332 Squadron at Leeuwarden. All Dutch F-16s are used in the strike/interceptor role, although 306 Squadron also operates in the reconnaissance role. For the latter duties, its aircraft can carry Orpheus recce pods formerly used on some F-104Gs, although it is due to relinquish this role in the early-1990s.

The original Dutch order covered 80 F-16As and 22 F-16Bs, but in March 1980 plans were announced to increase the fleet to a total of 213 aircraft, the additions comprising two batches of 60 and 51 Block 15 aircraft respectively. Deliveries should be completed by the end of 1991, by which time all Dutch fighter squadrons will fly the Fighting Falcon. The service had hoped to order further F-16s as attrition replacements, but this had to be shelved in 1989 as part of a series of cuts made to the 1990 defence budget.

The third NATO air arm to receive the F-16 was the Royal Norwegian Air Force, with delivery of 60 F-16As and 12 F-16Bs commencing on 25 January 1980. Again, it was the F-104G which made way for the new fighter, and four units now operate

# Fighting Falcon Fliers

**Above: Examples of F-16s operated by Belgium, Denmark, the Netherlands and Norway fly in formation with a 50th TFW/USAFE F-16C.**

the Fighting Falcon in the interceptor/attack roles, the latter including use of the Penguin ASM for anti-shipping operations. By early 1990, the Norwegians had lost 12 F-16s, but two Block 15 replacement F-16Bs were delivered during 1989, and another six F-16A/Bs will follow in due course as attrition replacements.

Three days after the Norwegians received their first F-16, the Royal Danish Air Force accepted its first example of the type. Of the four EPG nations, Denmark had ordered the smallest number of F-16s, comprising 46 F-16As and 12 F-16Bs as replacements for both the North American F-100 Super Sabres and the F-104G Starfighters then in service. A follow-on batch of 12 Block 15 OCU aircraft (eight F-16As and four F-16Bs) was ordered in 1985 for delivery in 1989.

Concerned lest early large-scale export sales hinder the delivery of F-16s to the USAF and its NATO allies, the US tried early on to restrict the availability of the aircraft. The first third-party air arm to put the aircraft into service should have been the Imperial Iranian Air Force,

which in 1976 requested no less than 160 aircraft. The first of these was to be delivered in March 1979, but in the event, none ever undertook the delivery flight. The Iranian Revolution early in 1979 was swiftly followed by the cancellation of all arms contracts – especially those with the United States – signed by the former Shah.

## ISRAELI ORDER

As things turned out, Iran's loss was Israel's gain, and the IDF/AF now operates the largest F-16 fleet outside the US and NATO. In the mid 1970s, the Middle East nation discussed plans for the possible acquisition of some 250 aircraft, and unofficial reports talked of an eventual requirement for between 400 and 500 aircraft. However, there were two problems: Israel insisted on early delivery, and it also wanted co-production rights. Cancellation of the Iranian order allowed the former request to be met, but both the USAF and GD were firmly opposed to the establishment of any production line in Israel itself.

Under the Peace Marble I programme, deliveries to the IDF/AF started on 2 July 1980 at a rate of four aircraft per month. These were suspended during 1981 in protest at the Israeli's habit of using its

warplanes in an aggressive manner. Temporary embargoes were invoked twice during the summer of 1981: the first followed Israeli use of the F-16 to attack the Iraqi nuclear plant at Osarik; then again following a series of operations against Palestinian targets in Lebanon. Until these hurdles had been overcome, the IDF/AF had to make do with the 53 aircraft already delivered, the final batch of F-16A/Bs not arriving until late in 1981.

In May 1982, the US Government announced plans to supply a further 75 F-16s to Israel. These would be F-16C/Ds, with deliveries starting in 1985, but yet another embargo was invoked – this time in protest against Israel's invasion of Lebanon – and it was not until 1986 that the first of the 75 aircraft began to leave the production line. All 75 had been delivered by the end of 1988, thus completing the Peace Marble II programme.

Peace Marble III, announced in August 1988, covers the supply of an additional 60 Fighting Falcons. Based on the F-16D and incorporating some Israeli avionics, these aircraft will meet long-term IDF/AF plans which originally envisaged operation of the indigenous, but now cancelled, Lavi fighter. The F-16Ds are scheduled to enter service from 1990/91 onwards, with the final

**Above: With three long-range fuel tanks in place, a Fighting Falcon takes off from General Dynamics' Fort Worth plant at the start of its long delivery flight from the United States to Israel.**

examples leaving the production line in late-1992.

The Peace Marble programmes have been matched by the Peace Vector programmes for one of Israel's Arab neighbours: Egypt. By the late 1970s, the Egyptian Air Force (EAF) was in dire need of new equipment, the Soviet Union having cut off supplies of arms and spares earlier in the decade. The only new equipment taken into EAF service since then had been a small number of Dassault-Breguet Mirage 5s paid for by Saudi Arabia, and a batch of Shenyang F-6 (Chinese-built MiG-19 Fencer) fighters.

Egypt turned to the United States, but its initial experience in operating US aircraft was less than happy. In 1979 the EAF received 35 ex-USAF F-4E Phantom IIs, but soon found that maintaining these aircraft was far more difficult than keeping their fleet of MiG-21/-23 fighters combat-ready.

The EAF finally mastered the F-4E, part of the problem having been the speed

with which this complex warplane had been taken into the EAF's inventory. Nevertheless, new fighters were urgently needed to replace stocks of Soviet aircraft. Announced in June 1980, Peace Vector I covered the supply of 41 F-16A/Bs, with several aircraft built for the USAF being diverted to the EAF each month from December 1981 to May 1983. Only the final ten F-16s were to be "custom-built" for the EAF.

The first EAF F-16 was handed over at Fort Worth on 15 January 1982, and the first batch arrived at An Shas AB on 24 March. Peace Vector II was already underway as the 41st and last of the Peace

**Below: The move away from Soviet-supplied military hardware led the Egyptian Air Force to adopt the Fighting Falcon as its principal fighter from 1981 onwards.**

# Fighting Falcon Fliers

Vector I aircraft left the production line in late-1983. As part of a $1,300 million package of military sales credits requested on Egypt's behalf in 1982, an agreement covering the supply of an additional 40 F-16C/Ds had been signed in May 1982. These aircraft were built in 1986/87, and EAF Fighting Falcons are now stationed at two air bases.

Peace Vector III covers a further 40 F-16C/Ds, plus a single F-16D ordered to replace a lost F-16A. This batch will be built in 1991/92 on a schedule a few months in advance of Israel's batch of Peace Marble III aircraft.

In numerical terms, the next most important F-16 operator is the Pakistan Air Force (PAF), contracts covering the supply of 40 Block 15 F-16A/Bs having been signed in December 1981. For years, Pakistan had been trying to obtain modern aircraft, but international opposition to the government of the day and growing evidence that Pakistan might be trying to develop its own nuclear weapons effectively ruled out the supply of US aircraft. Only in the wake of the Soviet invasion of Afghanistan did the the US State Department agree to supply F-16s to the PAF.

## HOLDING OUT

Initial deliveries were delayed by Pakistan's refusal to accept the ALR-46 (V)-3 RWR, the US DoD having vetoed the export of the ALR-69. Export clearance for the latter equipment was finally granted, allowing the handover of the first F-16 to take place in October 1982. Most of the aircraft were delivered within a few years, the final 11 arriving in Pakistan during 1988.

Soon after Pakistan placed its initial order, GD received its first, and so far only, South American F-16 order. The customer was Venezuela, with an order for 16 F-16As and eight F-16Bs to replace some of the Dassault-Breguet Mirage IIIE fighters then in service. The aircraft were ordered in 1982, and deliveries commenced in 1986 with a batch of six.

**Above: To date, the sole customer for the F-16 in South America has been the Venezuelan Air Force.**

With the F-16 in service with USAF units in South Korea from August 1981 onwards, it was hardly surprising that the Seoul government decided to order the Fighting Falcon for its own use. Deliveries of 30 F-16Cs and 6 F-16Ds commenced in early 1986, ending some three years later. A follow-on batch of four two-seaters is due to arrive in 1991, but a potential order for another 120 aircraft (72 of which would have been built under licence) to meet the South Korean's F-X fighter requirement was lost to the McDonnell Douglas F-18 in early-1990.

Licence production is very much a part of the Turkish Air Force's F-16 programme. Like Israel, Turkey has suffered from the effects of a US arms embargo, in this case following the 1974 Turkish invasion of Cyprus. During the late-1970s and early-1980s, a number of ambitious plans were drawn up by the Turks to enable the creation of a national aerospace industry and the production of a jet trainer, but sufficient funding was not forthcoming.

In the early-1980s, Northrop hoped that its F-20 Tigershark might be chosen by the Turkish Air Force, but instead it placed orders with GD for 128 F-16Cs and 32 F-16Ds. The Turkish Air Force was also the first NATO member (excluding the USAF) to specify fitment of the more powerful General Electric F110 turbofan engine.

The first Turkish F-16 was handed over in July 1987, and was followed by seven more GD-built examples. The remaining 152 aircraft are being built in Turkey by the TUSAS consortium, using new custom-built factories. Deliveries from the Murted production line started in 1988, and at least 36 aircraft were in service by the end of 1989. All 152 aircraft should be completed by 1995. The first 44 examples built at Murted are Block 30 examples, while the remaining 101 F-16Cs and 15 F-16Ds will be Block 40 aircraft.

At the opposite end of the Aegean Sea, the Hellenic (Greek) Air Force was also looking for a new warplane, but the final choice was postponed time and time again. Panavia tried hard to persuade the Greeks to join their Tornado consortium, but the field was eventually narrowed to the F-16 and the Dassault-Breguet Mirage 2000.

Despite the fact that the total requirement was for less than 100 aircraft, Greece eventually decided to split the purchase and order 40 F-16s and 40 Mirage 2000s. The first of the F-16s (34 F-16Cs and 6 F-16Ds) was delivered in November 1988, some eight months after the first of the French fighters had arrived.

A supplementary order for around 20 aircraft is expected in order to equip a squadron for anti-shipping operations, but it is impossible to predict which of the types will be chosen. In the longer term, the HAF needs to replace its Northrop F-5s and F-104s, but for the moment fleet levels of these types are being maintained by the acquisition of second-hand examples from NATO partners.

The Royal Thai Air Force (RTAF) is another F-16 operator, having ordered a batch of 12 Block 15 OCU aircraft in 1985. The aircraft were needed to counter the threat posed by Vietnam's new MiG-23s which easily outclassed the RTAF's F-5 fleet, and they were delivered in 1988. A further six F-16s were offered to Thailand by the United States in 1987, but funding for their acquisition was only approved by the Thai Government in October 1989. The aircraft will now be delivered in 1991.

The Republic of Singapore Air Force (RSAF) is another F-5 operator which decided to move up to the F-16, ordering eight in 1984. To date, it is the only client to have specified the J79-powered variant, but following Thailand's 1985 order for standard F-16A/Bs, Singapore changed

its contract to cover eight Block 15 OCU Fighting Falcons. These were built in 1988, and crew-training was underway in the United States during 1989.

The latest Asian F-16 operator is Indonesia, with protracted negotiations finally leading to a $337 million order for 12 Block 15 OCU F-16A/Bs. These aircraft, the first of which was handed over at Fort Worth in October 1989, are powered by the uprated F100-PW-220 turbofan powerplant.

Back in the Middle East, the Bahrain Amiri Air Force has become the latest F-16 operator. In January 1987, the United States offered to supply the type, and a contract covering the purchase of a dozen F110-powered F-16C/Ds was

**Above: A striking camouflage scheme as worn by the 12 F-16A/Bs supplied to the Indonesian Air Force. The aircraft are Block 15 OCU units.**

signed. Another four Fighting Falcons have since been ordered.

With F-16 production not due to end until 1999, and with a good chance of continuing into the 21st Century, the Fighting Falcon seems assured of a long future, particularly if developments such as the A-16 come to fruition. If the final examples serve for 25 years before finally being retired, the scrapyards may not be cutting up the last F-16s until some 40 years from now - over half a century since the F-16's first flight.

**Below: The Royal Thai Air Force has acquired 12 F-16s to counter the threat posed by Vietnamese MiG-23s.**

# INDEX